Declutter Now!

Endorsements

"Lindon and Sherry have given a true gift through the *Declutter Now!* study. It is a practical process, rooted in biblical principles, that will help followers of Christ structure their lives to be poised for radical obedience. I see this study unleashing people to serve in the church more passionately, give of themselves more generously, advance the gospel more broadly, and love people more freely."

—*Nick Ford, Senior Pastor, Northern Hills Community Church*

"Our LifeGroup went through the *Declutter Now* book and Study Guide. The Study Guide was very useful in helping us think beyond the basic concepts of the book to how it directly applied to our lives. The questions Lindon and Sherry have developed are thought provoking and facilitate discussion. The entire experience helped us find ways to take specific steps in decluttering our lives."

—*Jeff Fillis, Lead Pastor, Turning Leaf Community Church*

"This study has been a real and practical blessing – not just hearing but doing! Chapter One was so motivating and set the mood for the following chapters. I liked the stimulating discussions!"

—*Maggie Harding, Group Study Participant*

"I enjoyed that the Study Guide started with material things, so easily relatable, and that made it easier to see how our 'stuff' is much like our relationships, etc. ALL of our stuff, material, emotional, physical, etc., prevents us from being all that God desires us to be. Keep doing what you are doing! Thank you!"

—*Monica Stanley, Group Study Participant*

"This book and study have really helped me make great changes in my life and I have been able to spend more time and energy doing what God wants me to do – even stepping out of my comfort zone and sharing my love for *Declutter Now!* by leading a group study."

—*Tiffany Fehr, Group Study Leader*

DECLUTTER NOW!

Study Guide

8 Weeks to Uncovering the Hidden Joy and Freedom in Your Life

By
Lindon & Sherry Gareis

AMBASSADOR INTERNATIONAL
GREENVILLE, SOUTH CAROLINA & BELFAST, NORTHERN IRELAND

www.ambassador-international.com

DECLUTTER NOW!
STUDY GUIDE
8 Weeks to Uncovering the Hidden Joy
and Freedom in Your Life

ISBN: 978-1-62020-275-3
eISBN: 978-1-62020-377-4

Cover design: Matthew Mulder
Typesetting: Joshua Frederick and Hannah Nichols
Author photo: Vanessa Jayne Photography, Glendale, AZ
E-book conversion: Anna Riebe

AMBASSADOR INTERNATIONAL
Emerald House
427 Wade Hampton Blvd.
Greenville, SC 29609, USA
www.ambassador-international.com

AMBASSADOR BOOKS
The Mount
2 Woodstock Link
Belfast, BT6 8DD, Northern Ireland, UK
www.ambassador-international.com

The colophon is a trademark of Ambassador

Acknowledgements

WE OFFER OUR HEARTFELT GRATITUDE to Mindy & Norm LaCasse, Melissa Blumeyer and Tiffany Fehr. You shared our passion with others, brought our group study to life, and provided valuable insight and feedback. Thank you for taking a chance on us and believing in *Declutter Now!* We love you all and are deeply grateful.

TO MOM AND CATHERINE – From the start, you both encouraged us to complete the Study Guide, reminding us (over & over again!) how important a guide would be in sharing our *Declutter Now!* message. Thank you for your encouragement, vision, and faith. You both rock and we love you!

TO OUR AMBASSADOR INTERNATIONAL FAMILY – We thank you for your patience, commitment to professionalism, and care in all you do. We feel incredibly blessed that you chose to take on our project.

AND TO JESUS CHRIST, OUR LORD AND SAVIOR - You have continually amazed us by providing opportunities far beyond anything we could imagine. You are the source for all of our strength, motivation, ideas, and perseverance; apart from you we are nothing. We pray we use the gifts you've provided to bring glory to your Kingdom, today and always. Thank you from the bottom of our very grateful hearts.

Table of Contents

INTRODUCTION

Welcome!

WE'RE THRILLED TO PRESENT YOU with the *Declutter Now! Study Guide* – a guide designed for individual, small group, or Bible study application. While the *Declutter Now!* book was in the works, we were already itching to get the study guide started. We understand and appreciate the value of thought-provoking questions and the beneficial discussions they promote. We've been eager to provide a tool to utilize for digging deeper into the message we're so very passionate about. Honestly, we couldn't get it into your hands fast enough!

Keeping the Study Guide Decluttered

SHERRY'S NANA WAS A FAN of KISS—Keep it Simple Stupid. Sure, most people are kind and say "Keep it Simple Silly," but Nana Rose was feisty and she would say "stupid" . . . and she and Sherry would laugh and laugh. Through the giggles, though, the "simple" fact remained that often, things are better left uncomplicated. The whole premise of decluttering is built upon simplifying. Sometimes we equate simple with an uneducated approach or lackluster effort, but such thinking can seriously impede a brilliant but simple master plan or an effective outcome.

To keep with our theme of simplicity, we made this guide simple in its design. Not because we didn't think our readers could handle a complex structure, but because we didn't think it was beneficial or necessary. We'd rather save the challenge for soul-seeking questions and thought-provoking discussions, not for convoluted workbook-type pages that are daunting and confusing.

We love group studies. When choosing them for our own small group, we've perused quite a few along the way, only to put most of them back on the shelf. Not because the content wasn't interesting or worthwhile, but because the format and process seemed to take away from the material itself. Who needs excessive, overwhelming, and confusing? Certainly not the person who is trying to declutter!

We've also seen guides and workbooks where there's more reading than "doing," and this seems hardly more than the original book just being restated. Whether working through a study guide alone or with a group, the base material should jumpstart the thinking or conversation, but it's the dissection and discussion that brings the concepts to life.

That being said, for this guide to be effective, it must be used in conjunction with the *Declutter Now!* book. You should read each corresponding chapter in the book prior to wading through the related study material in this guide. This will give you the best return on your time and effort spent!

Group? Who Needs a Group?
WE ALL DO!

We've both enjoyed participating in small groups and Bible studies over the course of our lives and have just wrapped up our second year of leading a group together. Gathering together, corporate prayer, fellowship, and discussion are the core of what makes a group successful. Intimacy develops when brothers and sisters in Christ share their hearts. Ah-Ha moments of realization occur and new insights are gleaned when we interact with those outside the usual and familiar family and friends camp. Different perspectives are thrown into the pot, and horizons are broadened. Growth occurs at so many levels.

Acts 2:41–47 describes the early church:

Those who accepted his message were baptized, and about three thousand were added to their number that day. They devoted themselves to the apostles' teaching and to the fellowship, to the breaking of bread and to prayer. Everyone was filled with awe, and many wonders and miraculous signs were done by the apostles. All the believers were together and had everything in common. Selling their possessions and goods, they gave to anyone as he had need. Every day they continued to meet together in the temple courts. They broke bread in their homes and ate together with glad and sincere hearts, praising God and enjoying the favor of all the people. And the Lord added to their number daily those who were being saved.

These verses speak to the heart of learning and praying together, fellowship, and sharing meals. We would do well to follow this example and consistently incorporate these activities into our Christian walk.

That being said, though, if you're not in a small group or Bible study at the moment, this study guide is still for you. Thought-provoking questions, practical life application, and memory verses can easily be done on an individual basis. However, if you've never joined a group or study, we would wholeheartedly encourage you to do so. It's one of those "you don't know what you're missing until you try it" scenarios. We can tell you from personal experience that once you find the right group or participate in a life-changing study, you will never ever again want to be without that connection or opportunity.

Flexible Format

THE *DECLUTTER NOW! STUDY GUIDE* is perfect for an eight, nine, or ten-week format. If you have only eight weeks for your study, simply complete one chapter each week. If you have nine weeks to utilize, consider adding either a kick-off or launch meeting, or perhaps a "wrap-up" get together (aka party)! If you have ten weeks, implement both.

Not every group is the same. Some unabashedly dive deep right from the first meeting, while others take a while to venture below the surface. It can take time to develop trust and confidence within the group. This is perfectly fine as long as growth and forward motion is occurring each week. As we'll explain in the next chapter, we've developed this study to meet both scenarios, so wherever your group falls, this guide will be both appropriate and beneficial.

Invite Yours Truly

CONSIDER ADDING AN AUTHOR SEGMENT to your study. We're always excited to share our passion and are available to join your group in person (geographically permitting) or via Skype. We offer "Meet the Author" sessions to include Q & A time with your members. Some groups benefit from an enthusiastic launch, while others really enjoy meeting during the latter part of the study for the opportunity to ask questions that may have arisen over the course of the meetings. We'll do our best to tailor our session to your group's needs. Please contact us at declutternow@actionplanministries.com for more details. We'd love to hear from you!

Congratulations!

WE'RE GRATEFUL YOU'VE MADE A decision to either begin or continue on with the *Declutter Now!* experience. It's a life-changing, priority-revealing, joy-seeking journey. We pray the truths you uncover will bring you all the energy, joy, time, money, and freedom you need to live a decluttered life and to give God your firsts, serving Him with your whole heart and soul.

GETTING STARTED

For Everyone

Breaking It Down

EACH CHAPTER HAS NINE SECTIONS. Let's look at a brief overview of each:

KEY QUESTION

We begin each chapter with a thought-provoking question that addresses the heart of the chapter.

OPEN IN PRAYER

It's important to take a moment and focus your heart and mind on the study and the truths that God desires to reveal to you.

SNAPSHOT

A synopsis of the chapter's content and main points.

TALK TIME

A variety of questions intended to increase knowledge, promote growth, and encourage discussion. Each question is marked with either a pick axe or a shovel, indicating the degree of question depth. A pick axe suggests a question that *scratches the surface*, and a shovel implies that the question *digs a bit deeper.*

AH-HA MOMENT

An opportunity to reflect on a thought or idea that was particularly meaningful or impactful.

ACTION PLAN

What to do now? Where to go from here? Taking action is critical in getting you from 'where you are' to 'where you want to be', so put forth a solid effort with your Action Plan. Remember, a good idea will remain only that, JUST a good idea, unless you put action behind it.

MEMORY VERSES

Two verses to memorize during the following week. Beginning on page 113 of this guide are multiple copies of each verse to cut out and post where you'll see them most often – the fridge, bathroom mirror, work desk, car dash, etc.

DON'T FORGET

Wrap-up thoughts to take away from the chapter study.

OUR PRAYER FOR YOU

Our final thoughts and prayer for you.

**Note – When we reference page numbers throughout this guide, *unless indicated*, we are referring to pages in the *Declutter Now!* book that you are using in conjunction with this guide. **

Individual Study

WHILE THIS STUDY IS PERFECT for groups of all sizes, it's also an ideal individual study.

> Of course we'd say that, right?
>
> RIGHT!
>
> But it really is.
>
> With a few small tweaks, you'll be good to go!

The *Talk Time* 🕐 section provides thought-provoking questions for each chapter. We've provided an abundance of them to allow group leaders the ability to select questions best suited for their group. For individual study, you are welcome to work through all of the questions or just choose your favorites. Remember, though, the more you answer, the more you'll extract from the material. We know the over-achievers will run with it, but for those of you less motivated or fearful of what you may uncover, challenge yourself to a high level of commitment and discipline. We know you can do it and it'll be worth it in the long run!

You might find it beneficial to enlist the help of someone you love and trust for the *Action Plan* ⦿——→⦿ and *Memory Verses* 📖 sections. After you've spent the week working through the chapter, share your action plan progress and recite your memory verses to them. Another idea for memory verses is to type them **from memory** into a Word document or write them in a notebook. This way, not only can you check your own success, but you'll be recording the verses so they'll be saved in one spot for reference after you've completed the study.

Next, while the *Our Prayer for You* ♥ section in each chapter was written with a group in mind, please read through it. You'll notice that while we address the group as a whole, we're actually speaking to each person individually. We personally pray for everyone reading *Declutter Now!* and working through the study, so we promise you won't be left out. You are WAY too important to us.

Lastly, since you may not be part of a group study, we'd love you to consider starting an Action Team. This is a team of two designed to support, encourage, love, speak truth, and hold each other accountable. We've included information and the format for this on page 101 of this guide.

We're so thrilled you've chosen the *Declutter Now! Study Guide* and want you to know we're with you every step of the way. We'd love to hear from you.

Please direct any questions or feedback to:

declutternow@actionplanministries.com

Sign up for bi-weekly blog posts at:

www.actionplanministries.com

Join in on daily conversations at:

www.facebook.com/declutternow

Remember, the more you participate, the more you'll glean, so dig in and stay in. We're excited for you!

Leader Notes for Group Study

Additional Section Information

TALK TIME

We've found that a group of 10-20 people can usually work through approximately 7-10 questions in an hour, assuming the group is spending time discussing each of them. We've provided extra questions so each leader has the option to pick and choose the questions best suited for their group. You may prefer to (A) have the group complete all the questions prior to each meeting so they're prepared for any questions you choose to discuss, (B) tell the group in advance the specific questions to answer, or (C) perhaps save the questions for the group discussion and then encourage the members to complete any questions not covered in class. The choice is yours! You know your group best. You know the level of their openness and motivation, so we've given you different options to cover all circumstances.

AH-HA MOMENT

We've put this section in the line-up to assist the leader with the group's conversational flow. When discussing your group's housekeeping rules, it's a good idea to go over the Ah-Ha Moment concept. During discussions, it's inevitable that members will have something really hit home or experience a revelation. During the discussion, time may not allow each personal story to be shared or every light bulb moment to be addressed the second it's sparked. Encourage your members to write down anything that profoundly rocks their world and assure them you will give them an opportunity to share their most important "Ah-Ha" moment during this section. Sometimes you may have a few people share, and sometimes none, but at least the time is carved out just in case. If members know this opportunity exists, they'll be less likely to feel impatient and interrupt another speaker or become frustrated and unfocused when the group moves on to the next question and they haven't had time to share yet.

MEMORY VERSES

Assign your members to memorize either one or both of the verses. Encourage them to cut out copies of the verses found on page 113 of this guide and post them up where they will be easily seen.

OUR PRAYER FOR YOU

Please don't feel obligated to use this. If you feel led to close with a more personal, group-specific prayer, please do! If you'd like to use our prayer, wonderful! Please know that each and every member is truly special to us and we pray daily for any groups participating in our study.

Guidelines for Groups

WHETHER YOU'RE AN EXPERIENCED GROUP leader or a first timer, please consider the following suggestions, which are born from our own experiences as leaders and guaranteed to help you be the Star Leader you were meant to be! Okay, we jest a bit, but we do feel they're instrumental in getting your group off to a good start and encouraging a successful study.

Housekeeping

BEFORE YOU ACTUALLY DIG INTO the study, it's a good idea to go over some housekeeping rules. It's much easier AND less awkward to address group rules up front, and it might save you from some uncomfortable conversations later. Discuss items such as:

COURTESY

Take turns speaking, try not to talk over others, feel free to share, but try to be concise so others have time to share as well, and keep comments constructive and relevant. This might be a great time to explain the Ah-Ha Moment section.

TREAT YOUR GROUP LIKE VEGAS

What happens at your meeting stays at your meeting. Confidentiality is an absolute must—unless the member you are referring to gives you permission to share specific information.

ATTENDANCE

Yup, things happen, but for the group to form a cohesive bond, it's vital for members to attend regularly.

HOMEWORK

If there is reading to be done and/or questions answered prior to each week's meeting, encourage your group to make an effort to complete the homework assigned. The more prepared members are, the more engaging and meaningful the discussion will be.

COME PREPARED

Bring your Bible and the *Declutter Now!* book and study guide to each meeting.

YOU CAN CERTAINLY MODIFY THE above to fit your group's personality and needs, but covering any housekeeping rules up front in some form or fashion establishes expectations. People are more inclined to rise to expectations if they know what they are to begin with. Also, time is hard to come by, and you're letting your group members know you value their time and care about them very much. You're committed to the group's success as a whole, as well as the growth of each individual member.

If you add a little bit of humor when going over the housekeeping rules, you can have a lot of fun with it but also get your point across and set a valuable pace.

Rounding Things Out

1. PLAN YOUR MEETING FORMAT.

There are as many different group meeting formats as there are groups. There's no right or wrong, just preference and what works for you. For the sake of example, here is an idea of the format we often use in the groups we've led:

1. **FELLOWSHIP TIME WITH FOOD –** 20 minutes
2. **ACTUAL STUDY TIME, WHICH WOULD** include working through the first eight sections of the chapter guide – 60 minutes
3. **ANNOUNCEMENTS OR DISCUSSION FOR UPCOMING** events – 10 minutes
4. **CORPORATE PRAYER TIME WITH CLOSING** prayer (section nine from chapter guide) – 15 minutes
5. **FELLOWSHIP TIME, WITH FOOD AGAIN** (of course!) – 15 minutes

Our small group meetings generally last about two hours, but truth be told, we've been known to hang out in our driveway during goodbyes for another hour or so . . . even having driveway prayer time on occasion. Our neighbors never know what to expect from us!

Our biggest caution is to keep the actual meetings to the timeframe agreed upon and expected by members. They may have children to get home to, homework to do, or an early morning coming up. Be courteous and respectful of their time. The last thing you want to do is give your members an excuse not to return.

Also, if you are leading but someone else is hosting, be respectful of their home and schedule. If your members WANT to stay and chat, and the host also WANTS to visit, then they can socialize until 1am if they like. Just make sure it's mutual.

Again, there's no exact format to follow, and you're not going to please everyone all of the time. Nope, not even Christians! Just do your best to adhere to a format that works logistically for the study and for the majority of the group and you'll do fine.

2. RESIST THE URGE TO TEACH. KIND OF.

You will be teaching, but the key to a successful study group is dynamic discussion. And the key to dynamic discussion is asking creative, open-ended questions. We've given you many of these to choose from, but you'll also be forming new questions on the spot based on the group conversation. Listen carefully and look for opportunities to interject questions that will promote thought and deeper dialogue. Yes, there will always be threads of teaching throughout, but disguise it in the form of questions and conversation and you'll have a very interested and engaged group.

3. PRAY OUT LOUD TOGETHER.

This can be very intimidating for some, but the benefits are so far reaching that it's worth incorporating if at all possible. There is something so freeing and special about sharing your heart with your group and God through prayer—but some people may need to be convinced!

When beginning with a new group, we often pray the first time or two. We'll then stretch the group a bit and ask someone else to open and/or close for us. By the fourth or fifth meeting, we "sneak" in each member praying individually. When we begin explaining the game plan for this, we always see some squirming in the seats, but when members hear what is actually expected of them, they instantly relax. The trick is to present it with confidence . . . and speed! Ha! Here's how we handle it.

We leave 10 – 15 minutes for prayer at the end of our time together. We clarify which direction we're going to work around the circle or the room. We explain that if someone would like to pray, either to share a request or praise, they are free to do so. If they have nothing to say or are uncomfortable with the idea, they should simply say, "I pray for our group members," and they're done. That's it! This is a benign way of allowing them to take their turn without being embarrassed, but not putting them on the spot to do something uncomfortable. We ask that each person close their turn with "In your heavenly name I pray" or some other similar sentiment so the next person knows they are done. Saying "Amen" is reserved for the last person and indicates prayer time is over.

All in all, it's pretty painless. Our hearts have been overwhelmed with joy when listening to prayers from members we never expected would speak, never mind take such an outward leap of faith. In addition, we've had tremendous positive feedback from members who have expressed how much they look forward to and love the prayer part of our meeting.

4. GET YOUR MEMBERS INVOLVED BY DIVVYING UP RESPONSIBILITIES.

- **IF YOU NEED TO TAKE** attendance, give the responsibility to one of your members.
- **IF YOU CHOOSE TO HAVE** snacks or meals, encourage members to bring food to share for a weekly "whatever goes" potluck or assign a rotating schedule.
- **ARE YOU SHARING PRAYER REQUESTS?** Assign someone to send them out to group members via e-mail each week.
- **HAVE ANOTHER PERSON E-MAIL WEEKLY** meeting reminders or information about upcoming events.
- **JUST BECAUSE YOU ARE LEADING** the group doesn't necessarily mean you have to host as well. Is another member willing to open up their home?

Sharing tasks not only lightens your load but encourages participation and ownership in the group.

5. PLAN SPECIAL EVENTS.

- **GIVE YOUR GROUP SOME OPTIONS** for a volunteer service project and choose one to participate in together.
- **IF YOU HAVE A COUPLES** group, plan a date night out.
- **HAVE AN ICE CREAM OR** frozen yogurt night at a local parlor.
- **PLAN A FAMILY HIKE AND** barbecue or pool party together.

The possibilities are endless, but the point is to get your group involved with each other. Our small groups love our weekly meetings, but there is another level of bonding that occurs when we can relax and enjoy some social time together.

6. SUPPORT EACH OTHER.

If someone is going through a particularly difficult time, rally around them. If a member has surgery scheduled, organize a prayer time beforehand and schedule meals for after. Is someone celebrating a special event? Have the group members sign a meaningful card. A simple phone call can make all the difference in someone's world. There are so many ways to show you care, and your group can be a source of immeasurable love and support through the good times and the bad.

7. PRAY FOR YOUR GROUP.

Be in prayer for your group throughout each week. Ask God for the ability to lead them lovingly and effectively. Ask Him for their commitment and interest. Pray that you would bond as a group, meet each other's needs, grow deeper in the Word together, and uncover life-changing truths that will bring everyone closer to a decluttered life for Him.

Thank You!

WE PRAY THAT THE IDEAS we've shared will be a great springboard with which to launch your group study. The truth is that you know your situation and group better than anyone, so use or lose whatever works for you.

WE WANT TO THANK YOU for the commitment you've made to lead this study. The old "it's just an hour a week" is a complete misnomer! We are well aware of the time, effort, and heart necessary to lead a weekly study, both during the meeting but also in the time before when you are preparing and praying. It's a serious responsibility and obligation, and we are truly grateful for your willingness to serve.

Many blessings to you!

Chapter One

Having Everything You've Ever Wanted (by Letting *Go* of Everything You Never Needed)

Key Question: ⚷

WHICH ONE PHYSICAL AREA DRIVES you nuts and is in the most need of being decluttered? A drawer, closet, garage, storage area, etc.?

Open in Prayer 🙏

Snapshot: 📷

CHRIST WARNS ABOUT THE "MORE is better" mentality, contradicting what today's society generally promotes.

CHAPTER 1 OF *DECLUTTER NOW!* shows how LESS can actually be MORE—more gratifying, more satisfying, more manageable, and more freeing. Basically, more of all the good stuff and all that's really needed.

JESUS CHALLENGES US TO THINK beyond our earthly possessions and spend our time preparing for eternity.

WE AREN'T TO BE CONSUMED with the material things acquired here on earth. If we kept this at the forefront of our decisions and acted accordingly, imagine the positive difference in our hearts and lives, each and every day.

WELCOME TO THE FIRST STEP of your decluttering experience. We'll discuss where your clutter comes from and why it accumulates. Just as important, we'll figure out what to do with it and empower you with tools to get rid of it. We're so glad you've joined us!

Talk Time: 🕐

1. ⚒ **WHY DO WE** accumulate stuff? What causes us to gather, store, and sometimes even hoard?

2. ⚒ **READ MATTHEW 6:21.** What are the true treasures of your heart? Do your material possessions and the priority you place on them reflect what is truly most important to you?

3. 🪏 **DO YOU SUFFER** from a "more is better" mentality? Are you all about the acquisition? What consequences does this generate?

4. 🪏 **DO YOU HAVE** a desire to keep up with the Joneses? Does your competitive spirit keep you in an arena that would be best to avoid? What are some pitfalls of this thinking and behavior?

5. **IS THERE A** sense of security in hanging on to your stuff? Is there really any security in it?

6. **DO ANY DEEP-ROOTED** fears or concerns keep you in bondage and in clutter? Fear of not having enough? Not being able to replace? Going without? Do you cling to the past? Do you operate in survival mode?

7. **WHERE DO YOU** find most of your clutter comes from? What are your weak spots? Are you a "yard saler"? Does a particular store call your name? Are you an excessive holiday/event decorator? Do you obsess about storing up in preparation for a catastrophe? (Done within reason, this last one isn't a bad thing!)

8. **DO YOU EVER** feel suffocated by the mess in your home or in the abundance of things you have?

9. **DOES YOUR STUFF** hold you back? If yes, exactly how? What are you missing or enduring due to the clutter around you?

10. **THINK OF HOW** Jesus lived his life. Was he surrounded by clutter? Did he live to excess?

11. **WHAT STOPS YOU** from dealing with your material clutter? Time? Motivation? Energy? Desire? Fear?

12. **WHAT ARE THE** hardest items for you to part with and why? Can the group come up with some sensitive, creative ideas for handling this clutter?

13. **WHAT ARE SOME** modern ways to more efficiently store data and pictures?

14. **SET THE CUT** – what length of time do you think is appropriate to "set as your cut" for parting with unused items?

15. **ARE YOU ONE** who prefers holding yards sales or donating? Or both?

16. **IF YOU SOLD** the unneeded and unused items in your home, is there a good place for that money to go? Where would it be distributed?

17. **READ DEUTERONOMY 15:7–8.** If you donated items, who or what organizations could benefit?

18. **READ 1 JOHN** 2:15–17. How could we serve God more effectively if we physically decluttered? Be specific. Do you agree there's a correlation?

Ah-Ha Moment?

Action Plan: ○—→○

IF YOU HAVEN'T DONE SO already, take the Clutter Quiz on page 97 of this guide.

Have you uncovered a major roadblock causing you to falter in your decluttering effort? Sometimes it's helpful to address and conquer an issue BEFORE beginning to declutter. If this is the case, make use of the Action Plan Template found on page 105 of this guide. This template is a tool we created to help you work through a specific problem. If physical decluttering is needed, but you're dealing with an issue that holds you back, give it a try. We pray it will be a blessing to you, not only for this exercise, but for any problem you might be dealing with in your life.

FROM *DECLUTTER NOW!* PAGES 27-28, start your Project Management. **DO IT! THERE'S NO OTHER** way to start but simply GET GOING! And then be certain to follow through with your TRASH, DONATE, and KEEP piles.

Memory Verses: 📖

Then he said to them, "Watch out! Be on your guard against all kinds of greed; a man's life does not consist in the abundance of his possessions."

Luke 12:15

And my God will meet all your needs according to his glorious riches in Christ Jesus.

Philippians 4:19

Don't Forget: 👆

EVEN IF YOU FEEL OVERWHELMED, your Project Management plan will help you prioritize and start. A1 is all you need to worry about.

REWARD YOURSELF. A SMALL TREAT or meaningful moment is a perfect way to celebrate your progress and encourage the momentum to continue!

POST MEMORY VERSES WHERE THEY WILL BE SEEN AND READ. READ CHAPTER 2 BEFORE NEXT WEEK'S MEETING!

Our Prayer for You: ♥

WE PRAY THAT RIGHT NOW you feel encouraged and motivated. We pray there's an excitement running through your veins, screaming of freedom from the material clutter that has invaded your life. We pray for space around you to breathe and move within. God, we ask you to keep this enthusiasm going throughout the week and for the first steps to be successful. We thank you for each and every person willing to open their hearts and lives to this study and pray it will be worth every second of their time and energy. Thank you for allowing us to present our passion through this material, and we ask that you would speak through us, the group leaders, and the discussion, to touch lives for positive change. It's in your precious name we pray, AMEN.

Chapter Two

Lovers, Lifesavers, Leeches, Losers, and Lost Causes

Key Question: ⚷—
WHEN YOU THINK OF SOMEONE you'd either love to spend more time with—or perhaps far less time with—who comes to mind?

Open in Prayer 🙏

Snapshot: 📷
RELATIONSHIPS, IN MANY RESPECTS, ARE the most challenging to declutter. Instead of debating whether to discard an old kitchen appliance or pass on the new power tool you're dying to have, you're dealing with real people, their unique personalities, and a range of emotions. This is heart stuff, and it can be tough. Think about what decluttering your ENTIRE life means to you. While making physical room is critical to the entire process, making room in your life for the relationships that matter most and letting go of those that don't is just as crucial.

MANAGING RELATIONSHIPS ISN'T OFTEN EASY, and chances are just the discussion alone may make you uncomfortable at times, but it's worth the effort and discomfort. It's important to make all your choices count, and count well. Life isn't a dress rehearsal; it's the "real deal" in "real time."

SO, ROLL UP YOUR SLEEVES and jump in to discuss your lovers, lifesavers, leeches, losers, and lost causes.

Talk Time: 🕐

1. ⌃ **IGNORE THE TEXTBOOK** definition of friend and share from your heart what a friend means to you.

2. ⌃ **PROVERBS 27:17 SAYS,** "As iron sharpens iron, so one man sharpens another." In your own words, what does this mean to you? How do we "sharpen" each other? Should we? Do you feel called to do this?

3. ⛏ **WHAT PROMPTS YOU** to spend time with those who bring you down or frustrate you?

4. ⛏ **IS THERE ROOM** in your life to spend more time with the people who lift you up and bring joy to your life? How can you make this a priority and reality?

5. ⛏ **WHAT SPECIFICALLY HOLDS** you back from making necessary changes? Fear? Insecurity? Knowledge? Guilt?

6. ⚒ **WHAT RESPONSIBILITIES DO** you feel you have as a friend? "A righteous man is cautious in friendship, but the way of the wicked leads them astray" (Proverbs 12:26). Does this stress you out? Encourage and excite you?

7. ⚒ **WHAT DOES THE** term "professional victim" mean to you? Do you know any? Are you one?

8. ⚒ **HE WHO WALKS** with the wise grows wise, but a companion of fools suffers harm" (Proverbs 13:20). What does this tell you about the company you keep? Do you sometimes choose to ignore this concept because it might stop you from having what you perceive to be "fun," or does it help you stay on the straight and narrow?

9. ⚒ **WHAT PERSONAL RESOURCES** do you "give away" when you keep company with those who drain you?

10. ⚒ **HAVE YOU HAD** any friends who caused you to stumble or stray? Whose fault was it? How did you handle it? Have you been that person to someone else?

11. ⚒ **EXPLAIN THE DIFFERENCE** between a "hand up" and a "hand out."

12. ⚒ **REVIEW THE CATEGORY METHOD** on pages 55-56. Discuss the shifts you desire to make. If any members have a difficult situation to handle, have the group engage in role play to run through some different potential scenarios.

13. **WHEN CONSIDERING DOWNWARD** shifts using the category method, is there guilt involved? Can the group share ideas to make these transitions easier?

14. **WHEN MAKING CATEGORY** shifts, do you prefer gradual, subtle changes, or are you more inclined to make quick, swift ones?

15. **DO YOU HAVE** a person in your life whom you know you need to cut out? Are you prepared to put action behind that desire? If not, what steps can you take to prepare and equip yourself?

16. **READ EPHESIANS 6:10–18** on the Armor of God. What does this suggest about protecting yourself from evil? Does this make you feel more self-assured in removing a negative person from your life?

17. **DO YOU FEEL** obligated to help people? Can this be both a positive and negative desire? Explain.

18. **DISCUSS THE DIFFERENCE** between being a "lead-er" and a "lead-ee." Which way do you tend to lean?

19. **THERE'S A TIME** and a place for a personal phone call, a text, or an e-mail. Discuss when each is best utilized and most appropriate.

20. ✕ **WHAT DOES "LOST** in translation" mean to you? How can information be misrepresented through the written word?

21. ✕ **DO YOU FEEL** people can hide behind different forms of communication? How can attitudes and approaches be impacted?

22. ✕ **HAS THE IMPACT** from social media improved communication? Why or why not?

23. ⚲ **NOT ONLY IS** who we spend our time with important but also where we spend our time. Discuss some traps and pitfalls that can negatively affect your personal standards and relationships.

24. ⚲ **RECAP PAGES 70-71** and discuss the concept of "Freedom within Boundaries." Have you ever thought of freedom this way before? Can you add another example of why this works?

25. ✕ **READ MATTHEW 11:28–30.** Jesus WANTS us to share our burdens with Him. Are you willing to give your relationship concerns over to Him and allow Him to lighten your load?

Ah-Ha Moment?

Action Plan: A ⟶ B

EMOTIONS CAN SOMETIMES GET THE best of us. Walking through a problem methodically and rationally can be a great help when sorting through confusing feelings. As in Chapter 1, utilize the Action Plan Template on page 105 of this guide if you need assistance BEFORE beginning to declutter your relationships. The steps provided will help you clarify gray areas and shed light on what should or shouldn't be done.

FROM *DECLUTTER NOW!* PAGES 55-56, formulate and implement the category method. We've provided a Category Method Worksheet on page 107-111 of this guide to help you get started.

Pray for the changes you must make and the ability to make them. Be unashamed and confident in your actions.

Memory Verses: 📖

As iron sharpens iron, so one man sharpens another.

Proverbs 27:17

I can do everything through Him who gives me strength.

Philippians 4:13

Don't Forget: ✊

SPEND SOME TIME IN PRAYER, considering the relationships in your life. Use the category method to help you address and manage them.

POST MEMORY VERSES WHERE THEY WILL BE SEEN AND READ.

READ CHAPTER 3 BEFORE NEXT WEEK'S MEETING!

Our Prayer for You:

LORD, WE LIFT UP EACH person embarking on this relationship declut-tering journey. We know this isn't an easy undertaking, and we ask that you be at the forefront of all decisions and actions. We pray for temperance and compassion coupled with discernment and strength. Father God, we know that you have given us all the tools needed to make the right choices, and we pray for the wisdom to seek out your Word and follow your example. We thank you for the opportunity to share our hearts and passion for decluttering, and we pray that you would speak through our words to shine light on any darkness. We thank you for the group leaders presenting the material and facilitating the discussion. They are true and faithful servants. It's in your precious name we pray, AMEN.

Chapter Three

Divorcing Debt and Marrying Financial Freedom

Key Question: ⌀—⚷

HAVE YOU EVER THOUGHT OF finances in terms of something that may need to be decluttered, i.e., removing debt and unnecessary spending so you can attain financial freedom?

Open in Prayer 🙏

Snapshot: 📷

AMERICANS HAVE A PENCHANT FOR "accumulating stuff and doing stuff," and along with that comes the financial burden of paying for it all. A mismanaged budget and excessive financial obligations can hold you hostage to a life of struggle, misery, and disappointment. Since this clutter is just as destructive as clutter in other areas of your life, you must shed the financial chains that bind as an integral part of the overall decluttering process.

GOD TALKS LONG AND HARD about steering clear of the love of money and avoiding the pursuit of the almighty dollar. In Chapter 3 we provide strategies, ideas, and tips to declutter the financial chaos you may be living with. Even if you're in pretty good shape, let's make what you have work harder and smarter for you. It's not necessarily about making more money but often about doing more with what you have. Ultimately, we'd love to see you do more with less!

REGARDLESS OF YOUR FINANCIAL POSITION, there are always improvements that can be made. Light bulb moments that reveal previously hidden truths are like tiny gold nuggets of wealth, saving you big money without costing you a dime. Keeping this in mind, let's dig in and tackle Divorcing Debt and Marrying Financial Freedom!

Talk Time: 🕐

1. 🔨 **READ HEBREWS 13:5.** What do you make of the correlation between the love of money and God's promise to always be by our side?

2. 🔨 **CAN MONEY TRULY** buy contentment? If your initial reaction is 'no', think about how good, even temporarily, some purchases feel and then answer again. Should we feel guilty about this?

3. 🔨 **CHANGING YOUR SPENDING** habits requires not only a new budget, but a new attitude. Which do you think is more difficult to implement and why?

4. ⚒ **IS IT EASIER** to recognize irresponsible spending in others than to detect it in yourself?

5. ⚒ **DID YOU "TRACK** the Spending Trail" as *Declutter Now!* suggested on page 78? If so, what did you learn?

6. ⚒ **DO YOU CURRENTLY** have a budget? Why or why not?

7. ⚒ **IF YOU ARE** running in the red, what can you implement to reduce debt and expenses?

8. ⚒ **IF YOU ARE** running in the black, how can you be wise with the money left over?

9. ⚒ **GOD ENTRUSTS US** with the responsibility to take care of—and be accountable for—the blessings He's given us. How do you relate this to your responsibility in handling your finances?

10. ⚒ **ARE YOU AN** impulsive spender? If so, how can you curb this destructive behavior? Is this something you can manage on your own, or would it be beneficial to seek additional help and resources?

11. ⚒ **IF YOU'RE MARRIED,** do you have a threshold dollar amount established that prompts a conversation when either of you desires to make a purchase in excess of that amount? If not, would you consider doing so? Why or why not?

12. **HOW DO YOU** feel about coupons? Are they money savers or time wasters?

13. **WHAT COUPONS DO** you find helpful aside from grocery store food coupons?

14. **DO YOU HAVE** any tips to share for money-saving entertainment ideas? Websites that offer great coupons? Places to find incredible deals?

15. **DO YOU FIND** it difficult to give beyond your time and talents and reach into your pocket? If yes, what do you think prevents you from being comfortable with this type of giving? Is it necessary? Should you be comfortable with it?

16. **SHARE A STORY** of a lesson learned from a time when money was tight and you walked away with a new perspective about what was truly important.

17. **DO YOU THINK** you could be more effective for God's kingdom if your finances were in better shape?

18. **1 TIMOTHY 6:7–10** is a popular verse addressing the root of all evil. Read it and discuss: "Is money the true root?"

Ah-Ha Moment?

Action Plan:

IF YOU DON'T HAVE A budget, it's time to create one. If you already have a budget in place, review it carefully, checking for any updates necessary. To be effective, your budget must be accurate and realistic. Be sure you've done the "Track the Spending Trail" exercise on page 78 before creating or revising your budget.

MAKE INTENTIONAL CHOICES AND IMPLEMENT attitude shifts in order to meet your financial goals. Commit to a comprehensive attack.

IF YOU ARE MARRIED, MAKE sure you and your spouse are on the same page and are working together to attain shared goals.

Memory Verses:

Honor the Lord with your wealth, with the first fruits of all your crops; then your barns will be filled to overflowing, and your vats will brim over with new wine.

Proverbs 3:9–10

Whoever loves money never has money enough; whoever loves wealth is never satisfied with his income. This too is meaningless.

Ecclesiastes 5:10

Don't Forget: ☝

REMEMBER THAT IT TAKES A comprehensive approach, a new paradigm in your heart and mind as well as in your budget, to effect positive, permanent financial change.

THE IMPROVEMENTS AND PROGRESS YOU make will not only better your current financial situation and future outlook but will also open up doors of opportunity to serve God in a capacity you may never have imagined was possible.

POST MEMORY VERSES WHERE THEY WILL BE SEEN AND READ.

READ CHAPTER 4 BEFORE NEXT WEEK'S MEETING!

Our Prayer for You: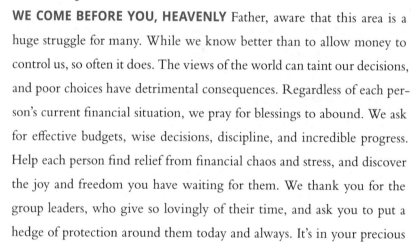

WE COME BEFORE YOU, HEAVENLY Father, aware that this area is a huge struggle for many. While we know better than to allow money to control us, so often it does. The views of the world can taint our decisions, and poor choices have detrimental consequences. Regardless of each person's current financial situation, we pray for blessings to abound. We ask for effective budgets, wise decisions, discipline, and incredible progress. Help each person find relief from financial chaos and stress, and discover the joy and freedom you have waiting for them. We thank you for the group leaders, who give so lovingly of their time, and ask you to put a hedge of protection around them today and always. It's in your precious name we pray, AMEN.

Chapter Four

If the Buck Stops, What Can You Start?

Key Question: O━━━

WHEN CHOOSING CAREER PATHS, WHAT single desire do you think motivates people most?

Open in Prayer

Snapshot:

MANY OF US ARE SO caught up in the "hamster wheel" of life that we pass on the opportunity to think outside the cage we're living in. Today, however, we're going to do just that. Since we have this time together, let's take a break, hop off the wheel for a bit, and allow ourselves the freedom and joy of thinking "outside the cage."

DECLUTTER NOW! **BEGAN WHEN WE** asked ourselves, "What would we do if money didn't matter?" That's like one of those "What would you do if you won the lottery?" type dream questions. But we weren't just dreaming. We were planning; seriously planning. With the power of the

Holy Spirit on your side, nothing is impossible. Nothing is out of God's reach, so why sell Him—or yourself—short? Thing BIG!

THIS CHAPTER IS MULTIFACETED. WHEN it comes to your career, if you're not following God's call on your life, we encourage you to put an action plan in place and make the changes you feel led to make. If you're already blessed in your job and are exactly where you should be, then we pray this chapter will help you optimize your daily work life. Most everyone can benefit from decluttering within the workplace, which involves taking concepts from Chapters 1 (physical decluttering) and 2 (relationship decluttering) and putting them to work for you. (Pun intended!) Even the most wonderful work environment can often stand a little decluttering of one kind or another. We'll also explore the argument for being prepared with a Plan B—just in case you need it. In this day and age, nothing is guaranteed, and we're advocates for being "prepared, not paranoid."

DEPENDING WHERE YOU CURRENTLY FALL on the career satisfaction scale, Chapter 4 (If the Buck Stops, What Can You Start?) can either prove to be lighthearted and fun—or one of the most difficult decluttering challenges yet. This is one reason we're such strong proponents for small group and Bible studies. Look around at your brothers and sisters in Christ. You're in the midst of a wonderful support system! Don't be afraid to speak openly; gently offer opinions and ask for advice. We're ALL in this together—thank God!

Talk Time: 🕐

1. 〱 **ARE YOU SATISFIED** with your current work situation? Are you where you feel God desires you to be? Why or why not?

2. ⛏ **WHAT IS THE** driving force behind your current career path? Money? Status? Comfort? Ease? Familiarity? Convenience? Passion? Joy? Responsibility? Schedule? Status?

3. ⛏ **DO YOU BELIEVE** the measure of success in a job directly correlates to the dollar signs on a paycheck? Either way, explain your position. Has this changed as you've gotten older?

4. ⛏ **WE ALL KNOW** that money, to some degree, is necessary, but how we handle it largely influences our options and decisions. Luke 16:11 tells us, "So if you have not been trustworthy in handling worldly wealth, who will trust you with true riches?" What do you think "trustworthy" looks like in reference to this verse?

5. ⛏ **ON PAGE 111,** we discuss "If the buck stopped, what could start?" Fill in the blank: "If money didn't matter, I would: _____."

6. ⛏ **WHAT WOULD IT** take to get you from where you are to where you want to be? What would need to be decluttered, rerouted, or initiated for this to happen?

7. ⛏ **SOMETIMES IT'S EASIER** to see the big picture from the outside looking in. Do you know anyone you feel is wasting their time, effort, and talents in a position they should have moved on from long ago, or should have never even begun in the first place? Use this example to help you assess your own situation honestly, from the outside in.

8. ⚒ **DO YOU BELIEVE** there is a time and place for "paying your dues"? This could include sacrificing by working long hours, getting paid less than you feel you are worth, and/or compromising your morals and values to "play the game" in order to build a strong foundation or get ahead.

9. ⚒ **IF YOUR CURRENT** job was eliminated unexpectedly, do you have a Plan B in place? If not, what would it take to prepare and lay the groundwork for a 'just in case' situation?

10. ✕ **IF YOU'RE PLANNING** a career change but an immediate transition isn't possible, what "helps" can you put in place during the interim? Hint, page 119: "Implementing small but instrumental parts of a bigger, better plan will help keep your faith alive during the waiting period." What steps come to mind for your situation?

11. ✕ **HAVE SOMEONE SUMMARIZE** Teresa's point on page 119. How does this encourage you in your own life?

12. ✕ **POSITIVE REINFORCEMENT THROUGH** Scripture is essential. Share a favorite verse that speaks to hope and perseverance.

13. ✕ **DOES YOUR CURRENT** work environment require decluttering? If so, what types of decluttering would be helpful? Think not only of physical areas, but co-worker relationships, protocol and procedures, etc.

14. DO YOU HAVE your own work space, or do you share with someone else? If you share, are you frustrated with anyone who is a "clutterbug"? If so, explain the situation and see if the class has any creative ideas for diplomatically handling this challenge. Are YOU the clutterbug?

15. READ MATTHEW 5:11–12 together. This can be a really tall order. Is God asking too much of us?

16. HOW DO YOU handle conflict with co-workers? Give examples of situations you feel should be handled co-worker to co-worker, and which might be best handed over to management.

17. HAVE YOU EVER felt unjustly targeted in your work environment? How did you work through the situation and, if applicable, were you able to declutter feelings of anger, hurt, jealousy, and so on?

18. DO YOU AGREE or disagree with Benjamin Franklin's quote on page 128? Explain your answer.

19. HAVE YOU EVER brought your career questions or decisions before the Lord? Do you think God is concerned about your work life? Why or why not?

Ah-Ha Moment?

Action Plan: A ⦿—→⦿ B

DETERMINE IF YOU MOST DESIRE to declutter your current career path OR declutter within your current job.

IF THE FORMER APPLIES, BRAINSTORM about what it would take to get you from "where you are to where you want to be." Strategically map out the steps of your game plan. Consider all aspects such as education required, relocation necessities, family impact, budget revision, etc. The Action Plan Template on page 105 of this guide could prove beneficial in accomplishing this task.

FOR THE LATTER, LIST THE different areas that would benefit from decluttering and implement a Project Management list to accomplish the task.

CONSTRUCT A PLAN B, JUST IN CASE.

Memory Verses:

Commit to the Lord whatever you do, and your plans will succeed.

Proverbs 16:3

But those who hope in the Lord will renew their strength.
They will soar on wings like eagles; they will run and
not grow weary, they will walk and not be faint.

Isaiah 40:31

Don't Forget:

TIME WAITS FOR NO ONE. If you're walking through this life anyway, it just makes sense to pursue your dreams and follow where you feel God is leading, rather than wasting time in a job that leaves you feeling unappreciated, unproductive, and miserable. Think BIG and have confidence that God has your back; He knows what's in your best interests. Trust Him!

DECLUTTERING WITHIN YOUR WORKPLACE CAN involve more than just physical space.

THE ACTION PLAN TEMPLATE IS a handy tool for any type of problem solving. Put it to work for you!

POST MEMORY VERSES WHERE THEY WILL BE SEEN AND READ.

READ CHAPTER 5 BEFORE NEXT WEEK'S MEETING!

Our Prayer for You:

FATHER GOD, WE KNOW THAT in any given group, there are many different levels of career satisfaction—or dissatisfaction, as the case may be. We ask that you work in each person's life individually. Help each one to see areas in need of decluttering and decisions that should be addressed and made. Encourage everyone to have a Plan B, just in case, so we can be "prepared, not paranoid." We know, God, you are the ultimate provider, but you also charge and equip us to do our part. Help us to have our priorities in order, and if they aren't, provide us with the knowledge and willpower to make adjustments. We know that our work life is just as significant to you as anything else we deal with; no issue is too small or insignificant. We bring all questions and concerns to your feet, knowing full well you love us and care about every detail of our lives. We pray blessings over the group leaders who have committed to sharing your Word and their time. In your precious name we pray, AMEN.

Chapter Five

Temple Care and Maintenance

Key Question:

WHEN IT COMES TO YOUR body, have you ever considered that you need to answer to someone other than yourself for how you take care of it?

Open in Prayer

Snapshot:

"IT'S MY LIFE, MY BODY, and I can do what I want with it!"

WELL, YOU CERTAINLY CAN, BUT should you?

IT'S EASY FOR US TO become defensive, stubborn, or otherwise unreasonable. We hate being told what to do and how to live. We crave making our own choices. We desire freedom from obligation and covet independence. If you're an island completely unto yourself and feel you have no one to answer to, this might seem reasonable and justified, but as a Christian, the landscape changes drastically.

SOME OBLIGATIONS IN LIFE ARE warranted and healthy. God bought us at a price, and that purchase requires our indebtedness to Him. Just as we have expectations on God, he has some on our lives as well. It's only fair, right? We can count on his promises because we know God will never lie to us, leave us, nor forsake us, but we also have responsibility that comes with the gift of eternity. No, we can't earn our way to heaven and we aren't suggesting this, BUT as Christians, we should hunger to follow His will for our lives. God gives us clear directives, and incredibly, He even covers how to care for our bodies. God doesn't miss a thing!

IN CHAPTER 5, TEMPLE CARE and Maintenance, we discuss the temple God has blessed each of us with and our obligation to take great care of it. Decluttering the harmful and replacing it with healthy and positive lifestyle choices and behaviors will not only benefit our physical body but our spiritual walk as well. We continue to pray for each of you as you walk through another week of *Declutter Now!*

Talk Time:

1. **READ 1 CORINTHIANS** 6:19–20. Many of you may have heard these verses before, but have you ever really thought of your body as a temple?

2. **DO YOU THINK** God has the right to ask you to honor Him with your body? What does honoring God in this way look like?

3. 🔺 **DOES THE FACT** that you were "bought at a price" make you uncomfortable . . . or joyful . . . or neither? Explain.

4. 🔺 **WHEN IT COMES** to taking care of your body, do you try your level best, perform the bare minimum just to say you did, or make no real effort at all?

5. 🔺 **ARE YOU AWARE** of areas in your temple that need to be decluttered? Are you prepared to take that first step?

6. 🔺 **DO YOU THINK** society, in general, prefers a quick "fix-it pill" instead of being required to exert energy? This does not negate that there are very real instances where medications are necessary, but we'd like you to speak to medications that are used in place of addressing issues and having to make any type of personal effort.

7. 🔺 **IS IT WORSE** to have an addiction to alcohol, which isn't an illegal substance, or a drug like methamphetamine, which is? Spend some time discussing the distinctions as well as the similarities you feel are important.

8. 🔺 **IN 1 CORINTHIANS** 3:17, Paul speaks of the temple and believer(s) in another sense. "If anyone destroys God's temple, God will destroy that person; for God's temple is sacred, and you are that temple." Who does *you* refer to in this verse? How does this use of the word temple differ from what we've been discussing in this chapter thus far?

9. HAVE YOU EVER had a serious issue with getting adequate sleep? What do you believe are ramifications of sleep deprivation?

10. DO YOU THINK there is a correlation between stress and physical ailments? If yes, share which conditions you feel can be directly attributed to stress. Have you personally ever endured physical consequences to stress?

11. DO YOU CURRENTLY have an exercise routine? If not, what is deterring you? If you do, is it working, or does it need revision?

12. HOW DO YOU combat a "glass is half empty" moment when you feel discouraged or down? Do you have a favorite "fix" or Bible verse to share that you lean on during these times?

13. THE RULES FOR eating healthy always seem to be changing. Do you find it difficult to discern what's healthy to eat and what isn't? How do you handle this?

14. DO YOU EVER struggle with positive self-image? Has your life's journey gotten easier or harder in this respect? If you are comfortable explaining, please do so!

15. FROM PAGE 152, do you know any "attractive" temples whom you fear are housing empty tombs? What can Christians do to make a difference in the life of unbelievers who seem consumed with momentary and surface beauty rather than the splendor of eternity? Discuss ideas for sharing God's love that might be relatable and interesting.

16. ⚒ **COMPARE AND CONTRAST** God's standards for our temples versus the world's.

17. ⛏ **DO YOU THINK** there is a correlation between your health and your ability to minister and serve God's kingdom? Why or why not? Along with discussing your actual physical capacity, also consider your witness and credibility.

18. ⚒ **3 JOHN 1:2** says, "Dear friend, I pray that you may enjoy good health and that all may go well with you, even as your soul is getting along well." The apostle John is writing a personal note to Gaius, a prominent Christian back in the day. This opening suggests that John was concerned for BOTH Gaius's physical and spiritual well-being, just as God is concerned for our body AND our soul. Do you think that one is just as important as the other to God? Why or why not?

Ah-Ha Moment? 💡

Action Plan: A●⟶B●

HONESTLY EVALUATE WHAT PHYSICAL PROBLEMS you need to tackle. Notice the word need. You may not WANT to declutter some of the issues with your temple, but they may still NEED to be dealt with.

SEEK OUT SUPPORT AND RESOURCES that will help you accomplish the desired end result. Don't be shy or afraid to reach out. No issue is too big or small for help if you need it. Just as with weight loss, the last ten pounds can be the hardest, so don't minimize your task at hand.

STAY STEADFAST IN YOUR EFFORTS. With physical challenges, if you follow a proven plan (whether you are dealing with weight loss, exercise, overcoming addictions, etc.) and do the work, success will come! The speed at which you see results can vary, but if you are headed in the right direction, it will happen! Hang in there and don't give up!

Memory Verses:

Therefore, I urge you, brothers, in view of God's mercy, to offer your bodies as living sacrifices, holy and pleasing to God – this is your spiritual act of worship.

Romans 12:1

Do not be anxious about anything, but in everything, by prayer and petition, with thanksgiving, present your requests to God.

Philippians 4:6

Don't Forget:

ATTACKING PHYSICAL PROBLEMS CAN BE difficult, and sometimes the fix isn't quick and easy, but God will provide. While you're working through your challenge(s), remember to bring your petitions and concerns to God. He is your ultimate cheerleader and will support you every step of the way; simply invite Him to do so!

THE ACTION PLAN TEMPLATE AND Action Team Guide are always available to utilize.

POST MEMORY VERSES WHERE THEY WILL BE SEEN AND READ.

READ CHAPTER 6 BEFORE NEXT WEEK'S MEETING!

Our Prayer for You:

FATHER GOD, WE COME BEFORE you today understanding our charge. We know we are to be good stewards of the temple you have blessed each of us with, but we also know that in our sinful nature, we can fall short. Lord, whether we are struggling with weight loss, healthy eating, addictions, sleeping problems, or anything else that might negatively impact our temple, we ask for the ability to see the areas that need improvement, as well as the motivation and strength to make necessary changes. Bless us with extra doses of perseverance and consistency! Bring people around us to help support and encourage us. Provide a path to resources or programs we may need. Father, our bodies are such a precious gift, and we desire to honor you with them each and every day of our lives. Your goodness and mercy knows no bounds, and we are grateful beyond compare. We also lift up our group leaders to you and thank you for placing them in our path. You are an awesome God of provision and love, and we are eternally grateful. In your precious name we pray, AMEN.

Chapter Six

Our Kids: A Decluttering Work in Progress

Key Question:

WHILE WE OFTEN REFER TO God as our Father, do you also view Him as your "daddy"? The parent who is always there for you; who scoops you up when you fall and whose lap you can crawl onto for comfort. The daddy who teaches, disciplines, reassures, encourages, guides, supports, and loves unconditionally.

Open in Prayer

Snapshot:

RAISING A CHILD IS QUITE a bit different than the physical feat of having that child. Sure, the pregnancy and labor bit is tough enough, but the actual upbringing . . . well, there are no labor pains in the world that adequately prepare you for what the next eighteen years, minimum, will bring. None!

WE HAVE AN AWESOME RESPONSIBILITY when it comes to our kids, but it doesn't just stop there. Even if you don't have children of your own, you are likely an aunt or uncle, friends with parents whose kids you spend time around, or a neighbor to families with kids. Chances are that somewhere along the way you're surrounded by little rugrats, or perhaps the older, teenage version. You may not even realize that you're already a mentor of sorts. If you have any contact with kids at all, you have influence and can make a difference, both good and bad.

SO WHY IS DECLUTTERING FOR kids so important? For us, the significance rests on the same premise as the life coaching we enjoy doing and feel so strongly about. You can prevent years of frustration, heartache, or failure just by sharing lessons you've learned and properly coaching your children, which will pave the way for increased peace, joy, and success. Yes, there are things our kids must walk through for themselves, and hearing sage advice doesn't mean they will take it. Disappointments and mistakes happen for everyone; they're necessary and beneficial to obtain critical life skills. That doesn't negate, however, the belief that setting a child up for success with a solid foundation is not only the best gift you can give them, but we believe it's your obligation to do so!

CHAPTER 6, OUR KIDS: A Decluttering Work in Progress, will get your wheels spinning. Whether you affect the life of a toddler or a teen, your influence, teaching, and encouragement can make all the difference in their world and in their future. And you know what? It'll make a difference in yours too! We lift you up in prayer as you begin the next part of your decluttering task!

Talk Time: 🕐

1. ⛏ **WHO ARE THE** children you currently have the most influence over? Give a snapshot of the relationship.

2. 🔨 **TO DECLUTTER OUR** kids, we first have to evaluate and declutter our own lives. Are you ready for this challenge? Sherry's grandmother used to joke, "Do as I say, not as I do." Why is this practice ineffective?

3. 🔨 **WHAT CAN YOU** do to make sure your home is a safe haven for your children? Discuss physical, emotional, and environmental factors, as well as anything else that comes to mind.

4. ⛏ **WHAT DOES "DFZ"** stand for? What steps can you take to ensure your DFZ?

5. 🔨 **OUR KIDS ARE** far more perceptive than we might give them credit for. Have you had a situation you tried to mask from them, only to find out after the fact that you were wholly unsuccessful?

6. ⛏ **ON PAGE 166,** we talk about "identifying the obscure." Have someone read the first two paragraphs. It's a tough list to consider; we're all guilty from time to time. Do any hit home? Is anyone willing to share? How important is it to address the obscure offenses? Why can they be so destructive?

7. ⌒ **IT CAN BE** difficult (for some) not to spoil our kids. After all, they're so adorable, right? If we overindulge them with material things such as toys and "stuff," what message does that send?

8. ➘ **ARE YOU GUILTY** of allowing your kids to "get away with murder"? This would equate to refraining from doling out consequences for inappropriate behavior or actions and not following through with punishments. What harm can come from this lack of proper parenting? Reference the following verses for help. Hebrews 12:11; Proverbs 23:13–15; Proverbs 29:15.

9. ➘ **THIS MAY BE** a difficult question, but have you ever encouraged or pushed your child to do something that meant more to you than it did to the child? This isn't ALWAYS detrimental, but it can be. If you're comfortable, explain your story.

10. ⌒ **HAS YOUR FRONT** door become nothing more than a turnstile? If yes, what schedule changes can you implement? What should be decluttered? How can you include your children in this transition?

11. ⌒ **LET'S GET PRACTICAL.** Do you have any decluttering tips to share? Space savers for bedrooms? Time savers for the morning rush before school? Schedule declutter-ers for the after school activity madness?

12. ⌒ **HAVE YOU EVER** thought, "It's just easier to do it myself"? Is it? Even when the answer is yes, should you?

13. **DO YOU THINK** parents can "love too much"? What does that concept mean to you?

14. **HELICOPTER PARENTS CAN** hover, over-involve themselves, and micromanage their children. Why is this harmful? How can you care for and love your kids responsibly without behaving as a helicopter parent?

15. **THERE IS AN** old proverb you've probably heard: "It takes a village to raise a child." Do you think this is wise? Necessary? Do you want a village around your children? Are you amiable to being part of another child's village?

16. **WHEN DO YOU** think your responsibility as a parent ends? Is there a certain age or level of responsibility?

17. **WHEN IT COMES TO** your kids, do you feel pressured to "get it right"? Why or why not?

18. **DO YOU SEE** God as a parent? As your parent? Explain why or why not.

19. **DISCUSS SOME OF** the ways that God "parents" us. If you need some ideas, reference the verses on pages 183–185.

20. **ON PAGE 182** we discuss the self-control God must have had in order not to rescue Jesus from the horrific fate that awaited Him; He certainly had the ability to do so. What can you, as a parent, glean from his example?

21. 🪏 **LOOK UP ISAIAH** 49:15. What is God's reassurance to us as his children? What can we learn from this to impart to our own children?

Ah-Ha Moment? 💡

Action Plan: A ⟶ B

THERE ARE TWO CRITICAL PARTS to this action plan:

FIRST, ADDRESS WHAT AREAS YOU need to declutter in your own life in order to be the parent and example God desires you to be. Examine your relationships, home environment, schedule, negative or destructive behaviors, selfish desires and actions, etc.

SECOND, CONSIDER WHAT AREAS IN YOUR CHILDREN'S LIVES need to be decluttered. Start with their bedrooms, clothes, toys, etc. Evaluate the balance, or lack thereof, in their schedule, activities, and social lives. Leave no stone unturned.

TAKE THE INFORMATION YOU'VE GATHERED and prayerfully and methodically work through each issue. Some items will be easily tackled, but others may take education, soul searching, grit, determination, and a whole lot of heart. For the love and health of your children, don't stop short. Seek out any resources necessary and commit to decluttering for and with your kids.

Memory Verses: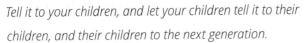

Tell it to your children, and let your children tell it to their
children, and their children to the next generation.

Joel 1:3

Train a child in the way he should go, and
when he is old he will not turn from it.

Proverbs 22:6

Don't Forget:

YOUR CHILDREN RELY ON YOU to be their mentor, protector, trusted confidante, encourager, and loving parent. Regardless of how difficult, uncomfortable, or challenging it may be, it's your responsibility to be the best parent possible. Learn from others you respect, seek the advice of wise counsel, and consistently reference God's role as the greatest parent of all.

THE ACTION PLAN TEMPLATE ON page 105 may be of particular help when working through a problem with an obstinate teenager.

POST MEMORY VERSES WHERE THEY WILL BE SEEN AND READ.

READ CHAPTER 7 BEFORE NEXT WEEK'S MEETING!

Our Prayer for You:

FATHER GOD, WE THANK YOU for the children in and around us. We are blessed by their existence and grateful to be a part of their lives. Help each of us to be the best parent, family member, friend, neighbor, and mentor we can be. Remind us daily of your example. Open our eyes, ears, and hearts to the truths of your teaching so we might follow your lead. We know how much your precious children mean to you, and we desire to care for them and love them just as you do. Help us to be insightful, reasonable, genuine, devoted, motivated, and faithful parents. We pray for keen awareness to any of our own decluttering that should be done. We know, Father, that change is hard, but help us to remember the primary concern and objective. Soften our hearts and strengthen our resolve wherever needed. We seek a welcoming spirit toward advice given and help needed. We praise you for being our Abba Father . . . and the greatest parent of all. We thank you for our dedicated group leaders who are walking through this study alongside us. You are a God of love, devotion, fairness, and discipline. We love you and thank you for being our Heavenly Father. AMEN.

Chapter Seven

Mind Over What Doesn't Matter

Key Question:

CAN YOU LOVE GOD WITH your entire mind, if your mind is a cluttered, stressed-out, and burdened mess?

Open in Prayer

Snapshot:

WHEN WE THINK OF SERVING God, we often consider the tangible ways we accomplish this. Volunteering, studying, witnessing, attending church, and tithing come quickly to mind. Luke 10:27 reminds us, though, that we need to bring God our everything, including our heart, soul, strength, and mind. We think it's especially important to note that God doesn't settle. Clearly, He isn't interested in a half-hearted effort or a partial commitment. He wants ALL of us – heart, mind, body and soul, and it's our job to do the best we can to meet this expectation.

WHEN WE ALLOW OUR MINDS to be cluttered with negative and destructive influences, we detract from the health of our overall well-being. While we all know that stress and anxiety happen and we all suffer from jealousy, bitterness, hurt, and the like from time to time, we don't have to permit these things to take up residence in our lives, and we certainly don't have to invite them back.

IN CHAPTER 7, MIND OVER What Doesn't Matter, we'll dig into recognizing the different types of mind clutter, help you understand and uncover where they stem from, and give you practical tips for saying good riddance to these debilitating emotions, behaviors, and patterns forever!

Talk Time: 🕐

1. ⛏ **STRESS CAN MANIFEST** itself in many forms. Name some of the ways stress can be seen, felt, and heard.

2. ⛏ **IS ALL STRESS** harmful? Why or why not? If not, give examples of stress that can be productive and motivating.

3. ⛏ **CONSIDER LUKE 12:25,** "Who of you by worrying can add a single hour to his life?" Could this be any more straightforward? (Okay, that was a bit rhetorical!) Even though the answer is clear, why in the world do we often ignore the simple yet profound wisdom in this verse?

4. ⛏ **WHAT CONCERNS IN** life cause you the greatest worry? Can you commit to relinquishing your grip and turning them over to God? What would the end result of this decision look

like? Visualizing a positive outcome can motivate you to get started and stay on track.

5. 🪏 **HAVE YOU EVER** experienced a time where emotional problems caused physical ailments? For instance, worrying about an upcoming test can cause a stomach ache. Share examples borne from personal experience.

6. ⛏ **IN YOUR OWN** words, explain what depression "looks like." What might someone be feeling if they suffer from depression? Why is it so important to seek help to manage depression?

7. ⛏ **FORGIVENESS IS THE** only cure to a root of bitterness, but forgiving is often no small task. Why should we forgive? Read Colossians 3:13 and Matthew 6:14–15 for ideas. What difference does forgiveness make anyway?

8. ⛏ **DO YOU GET** tripped up by wanting to reserve forgiveness for those you believe deserve it? Why isn't this good practice?

9. 🪏 **HOW CAN YOU** begin to forgive, both yourself and others, when you don't feel like it? Do you have any advice on how to begin the process of forgiving?

10. 🪏 **GOD NOT ONLY** forgives us, but He also forgets our transgressions. Read Hebrews 8:12 and 10:17. What is the distinction between the two? How would we benefit by following God's lead on both?

11. MOST PEOPLE EITHER tend to be extremely hard on themselves or not nearly hard enough. Discuss the downsides to both.

12. FOR THE PREVIOUS question, which way are you more inclined to lean? Brainstorm together on ideas to bring each behavior type closer to center.

13. ARE YOU A list maker? Can lists help with mind clutter? Do you consider them a valuable tool? Why or why not?

14. IN WHAT WAYS do you feel cluttered with mental overload? Do you find this debilitating? If so, how can you tackle decluttering the excessive, unimportant, unnecessary, and negative thoughts and emotions?

15. CAN YOU RELATE to the comfort and familiarity of hanging on to things that would be healthier to release? One would think it should be easy to let go of memories that are negative and hurtful—who wants them hanging around, right? But, this isn't often the case. Discuss why.

16. DESCRIBE WHAT EMOTIONAL contentment looks and feels like.

17. IF MOST OF us have so much more than we could ever want or need, why do we get caught up with wanting and

needing more? How does a heart full of envy affect us? Consider the short term as well as the long term consequences.

18. ⚒ **READ PHILIPPIANS 4:11–13.** Who is speaking here? What circumstances has the author endured? Would any of us think less of the author if he did complain? Does the author's position make him more credible?

19. ⛏ **THE LIES WE** are led to believe can take a terrible toll. We buy into lies that convince us we aren't good enough, we'll never be successful, everyone hates us, we'll never be happy, we aren't pretty enough, etc. Have you ever been victim to this bondage? If you've worked through it, what advice can you share?

20. ⚒ **ACCORDING TO PAGE** 215, who is our "Ace in the Hole"? Specifically, how can we lean on His help to resist becoming "devil bait"?

21. ⛏ **HAS ANYONE MADE** progress yet in decluttering their mind? Have you rid yourself of any mind garbage, stinkin' thinkin', bitterness, jealousy, envy, insecurity, anxiety, stress, etc.? If so, what does this look like in your life? Has your ability to serve God improved? How? Were there any unexpected benefits of decluttering your mind?

Ah-Ha Moment?

Action Plan: $\overset{A}{\bullet} \longrightarrow \overset{B}{\bullet}$

THOUGHTFULLY CONSIDER WHICH CLUTTER IT is that most consumes your mind. Is it stress, depression, anxiety, bitterness, jealousy, anger, and/or discontentment? Are you too hard on yourself, or do you have a hard time letting things go? When you read and discussed this chapter, were there any areas that made you wince or cringe? Be honest with yourself and pay attention to those red flags. Did you reveal any underlying issues that you assumed had already been handled, only to now discover otherwise? Perhaps you've uncovered something new that had never occurred to you before.

ONCE YOU ACKNOWLEDGE AND UNDERSTAND what you're dealing with, take steps to resolve this harmful, life-altering, joy-stealing clutter. If it's minimal in nature and a good pep talk, self-help book, and prayer will conquer the destructive behavior—excellent. Don't delay! If you're dealing with deep-rooted, serious issues, please get professional help as soon as possible. This isn't a sign of weakness or defeat, but rather a step toward hope and resolution. Don't be afraid, embarrassed, or lazy. Why allow something negative to take up space in your mind when, with a bit of work, you could free yourself of the heartache forever?

CONSIDER STARTING AN ACTION TEAM, which is found on page 101 of this guide. This section provides the perfect argument for having someone you love, respect, and trust walk alongside of you—and you for them!

AN ACTION TEAM IS COMPRISED of two team members who each desire to hold the other team member accountable, speak godly truth into their life, provide encouragement, and support their Christian walk. The Action Team Guide will help you get started in developing and enjoying a godly, mutually beneficial relationship with a brother or sister in Christ.

Memory Verses:

He answered: "Love the Lord your God with all your heart and with all your soul and with all your strength and with all your mind . . ."

Luke 10:27

Do not conform any longer to the pattern of this world, but be transformed by the renewing of your mind . . .

Romans 12:2

Don't Forget:

THIS CHALLENGE IS ONE OF the toughest. It can be easy to ignore what's going on inside and mask negative emotions and stresses with a temporary, cool, collected exterior, but you're not foolin' God. Be true to yourself and deal with the issues swiftly and effectively. If you aren't certain what treatment, if any, you may require, confide in a trusted friend, mentor, or pastor who can help guide you. When your judgment or vision is clouded, an honest and reliable person can step in and make all the difference in the world.

IF YOU'RE STRUGGLING WITH ACCURATE self-reflection, ask someone who knows and loves you. While they may not be privy to your thoughts, your actions and behaviors are helpful indicators. Someone close to you and who has your best interests at heart likely has some inclination of what may be cluttering your mind. At the very least, their feedback may inspire some ideas for consideration.

POST MEMORY VERSES WHERE THEY WILL BE SEEN AND READ.

READ CHAPTER 8 BEFORE NEXT WEEK'S MEETING!

Our Prayer for You: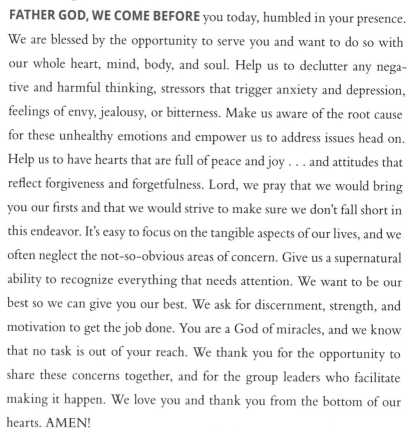

FATHER GOD, WE COME BEFORE you today, humbled in your presence. We are blessed by the opportunity to serve you and want to do so with our whole heart, mind, body, and soul. Help us to declutter any negative and harmful thinking, stressors that trigger anxiety and depression, feelings of envy, jealousy, or bitterness. Make us aware of the root cause for these unhealthy emotions and empower us to address issues head on. Help us to have hearts that are full of peace and joy . . . and attitudes that reflect forgiveness and forgetfulness. Lord, we pray that we would bring you our firsts and that we would strive to make sure we don't fall short in this endeavor. It's easy to focus on the tangible aspects of our lives, and we often neglect the not-so-obvious areas of concern. Give us a supernatural ability to recognize everything that needs attention. We want to be our best so we can give you our best. We ask for discernment, strength, and motivation to get the job done. You are a God of miracles, and we know that no task is out of your reach. We thank you for the opportunity to share these concerns together, and for the group leaders who facilitate making it happen. We love you and thank you from the bottom of our hearts. AMEN!

Chapter Eight

Soul Searching – Declutter & *GO!*

Key Question: ⚬⎯⎯⚓

WHEN YOU THINK OF 'Going for Christ', in both your relationship with Him and your service to Him, what comes to mind?

Open in Prayer 🙏

Snapshot: 📷

THIS IS, PERHAPS, THE MOST important chapter of all. Decluttering is the gateway to finding the time, energy, money, freedom, and joy you've been missing. But once you've uncovered this treasure trove of wealth, what do you do with what you have? As crazy as it might seem, this is where many people get tripped up. Being equipped to get a job done doesn't necessarily mean that you'll actually utilize the tools at your disposal. Think about gathering supplies to complete a home renovation project—but then procrastinating. All you've collected can sit untouched for months, or sometimes even years. If you haven't done this yourself, chances are you've witnessed someone who has.

WHY WOULD WE DO THIS, and how can we avoid stalling? Sometimes, when the heat is off and there's actually wiggle room to enjoy, you might pause . . . and then never restart. At other times, there might be distractions that re-clutter what you've just decluttered! Have you ever had an unexpected break in your schedule and felt lost, not knowing what to do with your time or where to begin? We're so wired for the constant "push" that when it's gone, we can feel lost and confused. This isn't uncommon, but it can be extremely destructive. To head this off, you need to be prepared AND have a plan. Even if the plan calls for rest (aka "doin' nothin'"), having guidelines, timeframes, and boundaries for how you plan to spend all the precious resources you've uncovered can mean the difference between success and failure.

REMEMBER, LESS IS MORE. IF you end up with "more" but do nothing with it, you would have essentially defeated the whole purpose of your decluttering effort. What a shame!

IN CHAPTER 8, SOUL SEARCHING – Declutter & *GO!*, we take time to recognize your accomplishments thus far, address the need to actively "GO," and discuss God-honoring ways to make this happen. When you immerse yourself in allowing God to use you for His kingdom and glory, everything will come full circle. Not only will you obediently answer the call God has on your life, but joy and blessings will abound as you live and walk in His light.

Talk Time: 🕐

1. ⌃ **REFLECT ON THE** areas we've decluttered in the first seven chapters: material stuff, relationships, finances, careers, physical

and mental health, and children. Which one did you find to be the most necessary and helpful? Is there one moment of clarity or accomplishment that stands out above the rest? We would love for you to share!

2. ◝ **PUTTING ACTION BEHIND** decluttering tasks will bring you more time, energy, money, freedom, and/or joy? Which did you yearn for most? Were you successful in attaining it? Were there any surprises along the way? For instance, were you cluttered in ways you didn't previously recognize or, perhaps, did you uncover areas you didn't realize you were desperately missing?

3. ◝ **BY DECLUTTERING, HAVE** you made the space necessary for God to dwell front and center? If so, explain the correlation between what you've decluttered and specifically how that has made more of "something" for God. If not, what changes are yet to be made? Do you have a plan for accomplishing them?

4. ◝ **WHAT IF YOU** declutter, but you don't "replace the space with God"? What risks do you run? Read the first paragraph under this sub-title on page 247 and discuss the implications the passage suggests.

5. ◝ **MATTHEW 4:19 SAYS,** "Come, follow me," Jesus said, "and I will make you fishers of men." What precisely was Jesus asking these men to do? If you were asked that same question today, right now, what would your honest answer be? Explain.

6. ⛏ **IF GOD ALREADY** knows our hearts, minds and souls, what is the true purpose of all prayer? What happens when we share our hearts with God and allow Him to speak to ours?

7. 🥄 **DO YOU HAVE** a harder time remembering to include God when things are going well or when you are consumed with worry and concern? In either case, discuss ways in which we can all remember to turn to God in both the good times and the bad.

8. 🥄 **READ MATTHEW 11:15,** John 10:27, and Romans 10:17. Discuss the important mutual message being conveyed in these three verses. Why is this just as important as praying? Do you fall short in this area? How can we train ourselves to improve our skills?

9. ⛏ **ON PAGE 227,** we discuss how God is actually three divine persons wrapped into one. Is this a difficult concept to comprehend? Share any thoughts that help you understand how God, Jesus, and the Holy Spirit are each separate entities yet encompass the same nature and characteristics.

10. 🥄 **HAVE YOU HAD** a "Holy Spirit Moment" you'd be willing to share? Is there a certain time when you are more likely to hear or feel His movement in your life?

11. ⛏ **GOD DOESN'T CALL** us to isolate ourselves from the world, but He encourages us to live in fellowship with our brothers and sisters in Christ. How do you manage this balance?

12. HOW MUCH INFLUENCE does what we see, read, and hear have on our spiritual walk and relationship with Christ? How can we live in the world but be separate from it . . . and should we? Are you ever convicted by the music you listen to or the movies you watch? Why is it crucial to make godly choices?

13. HAVE YOU HAD an embarrassing moment when listening to a song or watching a movie with someone? Care to share what made this embarrassing?

14. ARE YOU UTILIZING the gifts and talents God has blessed you with? If not, what's holding you back from "GO Time"?

15. NAME YOUR TOP three factors in choosing a church. Discuss why these are important to you.

16. IF YOU WERE the pastor of a church, what is one thing you would make sure was available or implemented for your congregation?

17. SHARE YOUR THOUGHTS on the church of today. In what ways has it changed from the church of old? In your opinion, are these changes beneficial or detrimental?

18. WHAT PROMISES DOES God make that you find the most comfort in? How do God's promises encourage you to strive to give Him the best you have to offer?

19. ⚒ **WE NOW KNOW** decluttering is a two-step process – Declutter & GO. Which part is more challenging for you and why? What can you do to commit to follow through on either—or both?

Ah-Ha Moment? 💡

Action Plan: Ⓐ——▶Ⓑ

IDENTIFY YOUR GO AREAS. NOW that you have "less" in your life of what doesn't matter, where do you want to spend your "more" time? Do you need to work on your prayer life, relationship with Christ, utilizing your gifts and talents, serving others, worshipping consistently, or perhaps staying in the Word? Where do you feel God tugging at you to draw closer to Him?

PUT AN ACTION PLAN IN place to accomplish the desired GO result. Ask God to help direct your path and give you the strength and motivation you need. If you need ideas, talk to friends and church staff who are active in the areas you desire. Make it happen!

BE ON GUARD AGAINST DISTRACTIONS. Ask God to reveal them to you and protect you from them. Satan loves to attack when we are in a period of spiritual renewal and growth. Don't allow him any foothold whatsoever.

Memory Verses: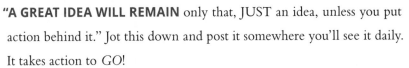

But God demonstrates his own love for us in this:
While we were still sinners, Christ died for us.

Romans 5:8

Therefore, I urge you, brothers, in view of God's mercy, to
offer your bodies as living sacrifices, holy and pleas-
ing to God – this is your spiritual act of worship.

Romans 12:1

Don't Forget:

"A GREAT IDEA WILL REMAIN only that, JUST an idea, unless you put action behind it." Jot this down and post it somewhere you'll see it daily. It takes action to GO!

GOD GIVES US HIS FIRSTS each and every day. It's our obligation to do the same for Him.

SHARE THE LOVE. If you know someone who could benefit from your decluttering experience and knowledge, please coach them on how to get started! And by the same token, don't hesitate to seek help from those who have already found decluttering success in your areas of challenge.

REMEMBER, THERE ARE HELPFUL RESOURCES available on www.actionplanministries.com and www.facebook.com/declutternow.

POST MEMORY VERSES WHERE THEY WILL BE SEEN AND READ.

Our Prayer for You:

FATHER GOD, WE ARE SO grateful for your presence in our lives and for your guidance every step of the way. We long to bring you our firsts, and we pray that we will always strive to do just that. We long to keep our lives clutter free from all that doesn't matter so that we can focus on what does. May our prayers be pleasing to you and our relationship with you grow closer and stronger with every word we say. Open our ears and hearts so we are able to receive everything you have to share. Lord, please equip us with all we need to take action: we desire motivation to get started . . . tools to get the job done . . . and consistency in following through. We know, God, that you deserve our firsts, but we often get caught up in the unnecessary and unimportant. Help us to decipher the difference and take a stand for what's right. Allow us to be used by you to bring glory and honor to your kingdom without procrastination or distraction. Father God, we thank you for all that you are, all that you mean to us, and all that you've done to save us from lives of despair and destruction. You loved us enough to send your son to deliver us from the grip of death, and we are eternally grateful. We thank you for each and every one of our class members, the insightful discussion we've enjoyed, amazing fellowship, and the guidance of our devoted group leaders. We ask you to bless every individual in this group. Place a hedge of protection around us and our families, and guide and direct our paths every step of the way. We love you so much and thank you for all you have provided. In Jesus' name we pray, AMEN!

Extras!

Going Above & Beyond with Your Group

AS YOU CAN SEE, WE'VE laid out the format for each chapter and have provided a comprehensive outline for leading your group each week. There are other ways, however, that you can individualize the study and bring your own flavor and flair to the table. You can magnify the experience your group has with fun takeaways, visuals, games, and quizzes. The possibilities are endless, but here are some creative ideas to help you get started:

Stickers

PICK UP A PACK OF chili pepper stickers and pass out one sheet to each member. Throughout the study, members can mark something that's a "hot idea" with a sticker. This way it'll make important points or tips easier to find and reference later.

Wristbands

WE HAVE *DECLUTTER NOW!* WRISTBANDS available for purchase at $1 each plus shipping; no minimum purchase. Encourage your members to wear the wristband for the entirety of the eight-ten week study. They serve as great reminders to declutter each day, are awesome conversation starters, and promote unity and bonding within the group.

Candy Bars

HAVE A CANDY BAR EACH week for the first person who successfully recites one of the memory verses from the previous week.

Launch Meeting or Chapter 1:

HAVE EACH MEMBER TAKE THE Clutter Quiz found on page 97 of this guide. It provides a quick clutter assessment that will generate awareness and spark great conversation. A perfect first meeting ice breaker and interest builder!

Chapter 1:

FOR A VISUAL, BRING THREE garbage bags. Tape a white piece of paper on the front of each and label them TRASH, DONATE, and KEEP. This will get your members thinking about the sorting task ahead of them.

DEPENDING ON THE SIZE OF your group, you can provide a clipboard for each member to use with Project Management on page 27. Perhaps personalize the metal clip on top with their name by painting or decorating it. We have found inexpensive clipboards at most discount stores for 99¢ or less.

Chapter 2:

BRING A SWORD FOR A prop when discussing proverbs 27:17.

PASS OUT PLASTIC STRAWS SO that each person receives one. Suggest that when they see the straw, they should be reminded to declutter the people who "suck the life out of them." (Maybe a bit crude, but we LOVE this visual!)

Chapter 3:

BRING A SINK STOPPER AS a prop to indicate the need to "stop the financial drain."

HAVE A PAIR OF SCISSORS handy and invite anyone who is willing, to cut up their credit cards.

PROVIDE A SMALL, INEXPENSIVE MEMO pad for each member to utilize when doing the Track the Spending Trail exercise on page 78. Pass this out at the end of the Chapter 2 meeting so the members will have it to use in preparation for the Chapter 3 meeting.

Chapter 4:

MAKE EACH MEMBER A PAPERWEIGHT. Gather up some rocks from the neighborhood and spray paint them. On each rock paint "Declutter Now!" and the Bible name and number from the various verses mentioned in this chapter. For instance, "Declutter Now! Matthew 5:11–12." Have each member start looking up the assorted verses you've chosen and then claim the paperweight that speaks the loudest to them. Whoever grabs first gets the one they want!

Chapter 5:

GO **TO WWW.HEART.ORG, THE WEBSITE** for the American Heart Association. In their search bar, type "Healthy Heart Quizzes." Choose one of the quizzes to go over as a group or to pass out for each member to take individually.

PUT A BASKET OF FRUIT together to use as a prop and a centerpiece
. . . and then invite the group members to eat your prop! Fruit = Healthy
PLAY EITHER THE DOVE "EVOLUTION of Beauty" video
(http://youtu.be/iYhCn0jf46U) or "Sketches" video
(http://youtu.be/XpaOjMXyJGk) for the group to view.

Chapter 6:

USE A MAGNIFYING GLASS AS a prop to represent how closely and
carefully the children in and around our lives are watching us.

HAVE A JAR OF NUTS to use as a visual. Ask the group if they feel their
children's schedule is "nutz"!

BREAK THE GROUP INTO PAIRS, being sure to separate husbands and
wives, to encourage the exchange of new thoughts and ideas. Take a few
minutes and have each pair discuss the biggest decluttering challenge they
believe children face. If they don't have children of their own, they can
speak of a special child in their life OR just about children in general in
today's society.

Chapter 7:

PUT THE NAME OF EACH group member in a bowl. Pass the bowl
around and as each member chooses a name, have them say something
positive about the person they've chosen. This may sound so simplistic,
but just a little positive reinforcement can go a very long way in boosting
someone's self-esteem. It's heartbreaking that some people haven't heard
a positive word in a very long time, if ever. This goes for men as well as
women! Is someone strong, confident, off-the-charts intelligent, funny,
caring, etc.? Then say so!

THIS IS THE PERFECT TIME to encourage group members to start an action team. You're almost at the end of the study, so this is an ideal next step to put continued support and accountability in place.

Chapter 8:

THE LAST CHAPTER OF THE book is a great opportunity for a special giveaway with which to remember the group and the study. Perhaps a bookmark with a special verse would be appropriate. Maybe a keychain or refrigerator magnet. It doesn't have to be expensive, just meaningful.

GO **AROUND THE ROOM AND** have each member share what they have gotten "more" of. Remember, the basic premise of decluttering is that "Less is More." What is the most important benefit that each person has realized from decluttering?

The Clutter Quiz

For each of the following, please answer yes or no.

DO YOU HAVE ANY AREAS in your home that are disorganized and overflowing with unnecessary items? This could be a drawer, closet, shelf, or even a room or garage.____

ARE THERE ANY PEOPLE IN your life that drain your energy and leave you feeling like you just wasted the last hour of your life?____

DO YOU EVER SAY "YES" out of guilt or obligation?____

WOULD YOU LOVE TO GO back to school or change career paths?____

DO YOU DESIRE TO BE debt free or at least reduce your debt?____

DO YOU EVER SUFFER FROM stress, anxiety, or mental overload?____

WOULD YOU BENEFIT FROM EATING healthier and exercising more? ____

97

DO YOU WANT TO INSTILL clutter-free living in your kids now so they can enjoy the benefits for a lifetime?____

DO YOU YEARN FOR MORE time with God?____

WOULD YOU APPRECIATE AN INCREASE in your energy, freedom, time, and joy to serve God in the way He has called you to?____

NOW, ADD UP ALL YOUR "YES" ANSWERS AND SEE WHAT YOUR 'CLUTTER SCORE' MEANS ON THE NEXT PAGE.

1-3 = CONGRATULATIONS! YOU LIVE an impressively clutter-free life and really have your priorities in order. *Declutter Now!* provides inspirational, relatable stories and practical life application. Since there's always room for improvement, and it's a great read anyway, dig in and give it a try.

4-6 = WELL, YOU HAVE work to be done, but there's hope, so don't despair. *Declutter Now!* will point you in the right direction and motivate you to get started reducing the clutter in your life. More of all you want is right around the corner, so don't delay. Small changes can make BIG differences!

7-10 = WELCOME TO THE club! Most of us, unknowingly, live with overwhelming clutter in every area of our lives. This prevents us from enjoying the life that God has purposed for us. We only get one shot at our earthly existence, so stop wasting your precious resources. Commit to taking action and making positive change today! Join us in the *Declutter Now!* journey and find that LESS is truly MORE.

Action Team Guide

AN ACTION TEAM IS COMPRISED of two team members who each desire to hold the other team member accountable, speak godly truth into each other's life, provide encouragement, and support their Christian walk.

THE ACTION TEAM GUIDE WILL help you get started in developing and enjoying a godly, mutually beneficial relationship with a brother or sister in Christ.

As iron sharpens iron, so one person sharpens another.

Proverbs 27:17

How to Begin

BEFORE CHOOSING A TEAM MEMBER, seek God's will through prayer and ask Him to guide and direct your choice. It's important to choose a Christian team member whom you know to be reliable and honest.

PERFECTION IS NOT REQUIRED! JUST a true desire to make a solid effort.

WE RECOMMEND THAT EACH POTENTIAL team member read this guide over before making a commitment so both are on the same page before making a decision.

Action Teams:

- Are made up of two members of the SAME GENDER
- Meet weekly or every other week
- Meet in person, via video chat, or over the phone

Action Team Members:

- Make a commitment to the team for a minimum of six months, maximum of a year. After the initial time commitment is over, a mutual decision is made whether or not to continue with the team. If continuing, a new time period is established.
- Agree to hold the other team member accountable, speak godly truth into their life, provide encouragement, and support their Christian walk.
- Agree to meet as planned and provide courteous communication if meeting can't be kept.

Action Team Meeting Guide:

- Open in prayer – alternate leading prayer for each meeting.
- Each member should bring a verse to share and discuss why it was chosen.
- Each member will share a high and a low for the week.
- Does either member have a challenge to discuss?
- What is each member's focus or plan for the next week or two? What does life look like?
- Encourage each other with constructive feedback, advice, and support.
- Prayer requests?
- Close in prayer – again, alternating for each meeting.

Please note ...

THE ABOVE GUIDE IS SIMPLY a guide to help you get started in developing a meaningful and beneficial action team. We encourage you to tailor your meetings to your unique team. If you feel led to pray during the meeting, please do so! If the Holy Spirit is nudging you to check on your team member in between meetings, pick up the phone.

THE MOST SUCCESSFUL ACTION TEAMS won't take shortcuts. Meet consistently, share honestly, speak constructively, and give as much as you receive.

WE ENCOURAGE EACH TEAM MEMBER to keep an action team notebook handy during meetings. Write down verses, information to help you follow up with your team member, and prayer requests. During the week, jot down any notes you want to share at the next meeting.

FEEL EMPOWERED TO TAKE OWNERSHIP and develop a loving and beneficial relationship with your action team member!

AS ALWAYS, WE ENCOURAGE YOU to share your experiences with us! Please e-mail us at declutternow@actionplanministries.com.

Action Plan Template

OFTEN WHEN CONSUMED BY A problem or struggling with a decision, our thoughts get clouded, emotions take over, and logic goes right out the window.

The Action Plan Template will help you cut through all the confusion and take productive steps toward achieving the positive end result you desire.

Action Plan Template

1. **PRAY. LAY YOUR BURDENS BEFORE** God. Ask Him for assistance in working through the situation/problem you're dealing with and for His truth to be revealed.

2. **IDENTIFY THE SPECIFIC DILEMMA. GET** rid of the unnecessary and zero in on what the actual problem is.

3. **RESEARCH WHAT GOD SAYS ON** the matter. Dive into the word and seek trusted Christian friends and resources. Understand God's position.

4. **DETERMINE WHAT ABOUT THE SITUATION/PROBLEM** IS within your control.

5. **DETERMINE WHAT ABOUT THE SITUATION/PROBLEM** IS NOT within your control.

6. **WHAT IS YOUR DESIRED END** result? Bottom line: what do you wish to accomplish?

7. **BEARING IN MIND WHAT'S WITHIN** your control, what steps can you take, while walking in God's will and word, to attain the desired result?

8. **CAN YOU LIVE WITH THE** steps it's clear you should take?

IF THE ANSWER TO #8 IS NO:

- **PRAY. ASK GOD FOR ENCOURAGEMENT** and direction.

- **SEEK WISE COUNSEL TO GAIN** additional insight or the support you need to move forward.

IF THE ANSWER TO #8 is yes:

- **PRAY. ASK GOD FOR THE** right words and constructive actions. Pray for divine intervention and his presence with you every step of the way.

- **CREATE YOUR ACTION PLAN. INCLUDE** the specific steps you will need to take, along with a projected timeline.

- **GET STARTED.**

- **SET UP CHECKPOINTS ALONG THE** way to track and monitor progress.

- **PRAY. THANK GOD FOR THE** ability He gave you to work through this challenge and for His neverending faithfulness in your life.

Category Method Worksheet

IN YOUR OWN WORDS, DEFINE EACH CATEGORY:

1 — _____

_____

2 — _____

_____

3 — _____

_____

4 — _____

_____

5 — _____

_____

6 — _____

_____

7 — _____

_____

8 — _____

_____

NEXT, LIST THE PEOPLE IN YOUR LIFE WHERE A SHIFT IN CAT-
EGORY, WHETHER UPWARD OR DOWNWARD, IS DESIRED OR
NECESSARY AND PRAYERFULLY FILL IN THE BLANKS FOR EACH
OF THEM:

NAME _____

CURRENT CATEGORY _____

DESIRED CATEGORY _____

REASON FOR CHANGE _____

_____

STEPS REQUIRED TO MAKE CATEGORY SHIFT:

- _____

  _____

- _____

  _____

- _____

  _____

NAME _____

CURRENT CATEGORY _____

DESIRED CATEGORY _____

REASON FOR CHANGE _____

_____

STEPS REQUIRED TO MAKE CATEGORY SHIFT:

- _____

_____

- _____

_____

- _____

_____

NAME _____

CURRENT CATEGORY _____

DESIRED CATEGORY _____

REASON FOR CHANGE _____

_____

STEPS REQUIRED TO MAKE CATEGORY SHIFT:

- _____

_____

- _____

_____

- _____

_____

NAME _____

CURRENT CATEGORY _____

DESIRED CATEGORY _____

REASON FOR CHANGE _____

_____

STEPS REQUIRED TO MAKE CATEGORY SHIFT:

- _____

  _____

- _____

  _____

- _____

  _____

NAME _____

CURRENT CATEGORY _____

DESIRED CATEGORY _____

REASON FOR CHANGE _____

_____

STEPS REQUIRED TO MAKE CATEGORY SHIFT:

- _____

  _____

- _____

  _____

- _____

  _____

NAME _____

CURRENT CATEGORY _____

DESIRED CATEGORY _____

REASON FOR CHANGE _____

_____

STEPS REQUIRED TO MAKE CATEGORY SHIFT:

- _____

  _____

- _____

  _____

- _____

  _____

NAME _____

CURRENT CATEGORY _____

DESIRED CATEGORY _____

REASON FOR CHANGE _____

_____

STEPS REQUIRED TO MAKE CATEGORY SHIFT:

- _____

  _____

- _____

  _____

- _____

  _____

Memory Verses to Cut & Post

ON THE FOLLOWING PAGES, YOU'LL find the memory verses from each chapter.

VERSE MEMORIZATION NOT ONLY INCREASES basic knowledge but also fosters growth in our relationship with the Father and provides depth in the Word we can all benefit from. What about being prepared and equipping yourself so God can use you? It's all important!

EACH WEEK, CUT OUT THE chapter's verses and tape them to your fridge, bathroom mirror, desk at work, car dash, wherever! Make an effort to memorize these verses by reading them over repeatedly throughout each day. You'll be surprised at the significant progress a consistent effort can make. Even if you don't commit the verses entirely to memory, they'll become more familiar and you'll be surprised at your recall ability.

Chapter One

THEN HE SAID TO THEM, "Watch out! Be on your guard against all kinds of greed; a man's life does not consist in the abundance of his possessions."(Luke 12:15)

THEN HE SAID TO THEM, "Watch out! Be on your guard against all kinds of greed; a man's life does not consist in the abundance of his possessions."(Luke 12:15)

THEN HE SAID TO THEM, "Watch out! Be on your guard against all kinds of greed; a man's life does not consist in the abundance of his possessions."(Luke 12:15)

THEN HE SAID TO THEM, "Watch out! Be on your guard against all kinds of greed; a man's life does not consist in the abundance of his possessions."(Luke 12:15)

THEN HE SAID TO THEM, "Watch out! Be on your guard against all kinds of greed; a man's life does not consist in the abundance of his possessions."(Luke 12:15)

AND MY GOD WILL MEET all your needs according to his glorious riches in Christ Jesus. (Philippians 4:19)

AND MY GOD WILL MEET all your needs according to his glorious riches in Christ Jesus. (Philippians 4:19)

AND MY GOD WILL MEET all your needs according to his glorious riches in Christ Jesus. (Philippians 4:19)

AND MY GOD WILL MEET all your needs according to his glorious riches in Christ Jesus. (Philippians 4:19)

AND MY GOD WILL MEET all your needs according to his glorious riches in Christ Jesus. (Philippians 4:19)

Chapter Two

AS IRON SHARPENS IRON, SO one man sharpens another. (Proverbs 27:17)

AS IRON SHARPENS IRON, SO one man sharpens another. (Proverbs 27:17)

AS IRON SHARPENS IRON, SO one man sharpens another. (Proverbs 27:17)

AS IRON SHARPENS IRON, SO one man sharpens another. (Proverbs 27:17)

AS IRON SHARPENS IRON, SO one man sharpens another. (Proverbs 27:17)

I CAN DO EVERYTHING THROUGH Him who gives me strength. (Philippians 4:13)

I CAN DO EVERYTHING THROUGH Him who gives me strength. (Philippians 4:13)

I CAN DO EVERYTHING THROUGH Him who gives me strength. (Philippians 4:13)

I CAN DO EVERYTHING THROUGH Him who gives me strength. (Philippians 4:13)

I CAN DO EVERYTHING THROUGH Him who gives me strength. (Philippians 4:13)

Chapter Three

HONOR THE LORD WITH YOUR wealth, with the first fruits of all your crops; then your barns will be filled to overflowing, and your vats will brim over with new wine. (Proverbs 3:9–10)

HONOR THE LORD WITH YOUR wealth, with the first fruits of all your crops; then your barns will be filled to overflowing, and your vats will brim over with new wine. (Proverbs 3:9–10)

HONOR THE LORD WITH YOUR wealth, with the first fruits of all your crops; then your barns will be filled to overflowing, and your vats will brim over with new wine. (Proverbs 3:9–10)

HONOR THE LORD WITH YOUR wealth, with the first fruits of all your crops; then your barns will be filled to overflowing, and your vats will brim over with new wine. (Proverbs 3:9–10)

HONOR THE LORD WITH YOUR wealth, with the first fruits of all your crops; then your barns will be filled to overflowing, and your vats will brim over with new wine. (Proverbs 3:9–10)

WHOEVER LOVES MONEY NEVER HAS money enough; whoever loves wealth is never satisfied with his income. This too is meaningless. (Ecclesiastes 5:10)

WHOEVER LOVES MONEY NEVER HAS money enough; whoever loves wealth is never satisfied with his income. This too is meaningless. (Ecclesiastes 5:10)

WHOEVER LOVES MONEY NEVER HAS money enough; whoever loves wealth is never satisfied with his income. This too is meaningless. (Ecclesiastes 5:10)

WHOEVER LOVES MONEY NEVER HAS money enough; whoever loves wealth is never satisfied with his income. This too is meaningless. (Ecclesiastes 5:10)

WHOEVER LOVES MONEY NEVER HAS money enough; whoever loves wealth is never satisfied with his income. This too is meaningless. (Ecclesiastes 5:10)

Memory Verses to Cut & Post | 127

Chapter Four

COMMIT TO THE LORD WHATEVER you do, and your plans will succeed. (Proverbs 16:3)

COMMIT TO THE LORD WHATEVER you do, and your plans will succeed. (Proverbs 16:3)

COMMIT TO THE LORD WHATEVER you do, and your plans will succeed. (Proverbs 16:3)

COMMIT TO THE LORD WHATEVER you do, and your plans will succeed. (Proverbs 16:3)

COMMIT TO THE LORD WHATEVER you do, and your plans will succeed. (Proverbs 16:3)

BUT THOSE WHO HOPE IN the Lord will renew their strength. They will soar on wings like eagles; they will run and not grow weary, they will walk and not be faint. (Isaiah 40:31)

BUT THOSE WHO HOPE IN the Lord will renew their strength. They will soar on wings like eagles; they will run and not grow weary, they will walk and not be faint. (Isaiah 40:31)

BUT THOSE WHO HOPE IN the Lord will renew their strength. They will soar on wings like eagles; they will run and not grow weary, they will walk and not be faint. (Isaiah 40:31)

BUT THOSE WHO HOPE IN the Lord will renew their strength. They will soar on wings like eagles; they will run and not grow weary, they will walk and not be faint. (Isaiah 40:31)

BUT THOSE WHO HOPE IN the Lord will renew their strength. They will soar on wings like eagles; they will run and not grow weary, they will walk and not be faint. (Isaiah 40:31)

Chapter Five

THEREFORE, I URGE YOU, BROTHERS, in view of God's mercy, to offer your bodies as living sacrifices, holy and pleasing to God – this is your spiritual act of worship. (Romans 12:1)

THEREFORE, I URGE YOU, BROTHERS, in view of God's mercy, to offer your bodies as living sacrifices, holy and pleasing to God – this is your spiritual act of worship. (Romans 12:1)

THEREFORE, I URGE YOU, BROTHERS, in view of God's mercy, to offer your bodies as living sacrifices, holy and pleasing to God – this is your spiritual act of worship. (Romans 12:1)

THEREFORE, I URGE YOU, BROTHERS, in view of God's mercy, to offer your bodies as living sacrifices, holy and pleasing to God – this is your spiritual act of worship. (Romans 12:1)

THEREFORE, I URGE YOU, BROTHERS, in view of God's mercy, to offer your bodies as living sacrifices, holy and pleasing to God – this is your spiritual act of worship. (Romans 12:1)

DO NOT BE ANXIOUS ABOUT anything, but in everything, by prayer and petition, with thanksgiving, present your requests to God. (Philippians 4:6)

DO NOT BE ANXIOUS ABOUT anything, but in everything, by prayer and petition, with thanksgiving, present your requests to God. (Philippians 4:6)

DO NOT BE ANXIOUS ABOUT anything, but in everything, by prayer and petition, with thanksgiving, present your requests to God. (Philippians 4:6)

DO NOT BE ANXIOUS ABOUT anything, but in everything, by prayer and petition, with thanksgiving, present your requests to God. (Philippians 4:6)

DO NOT BE ANXIOUS ABOUT anything, but in everything, by prayer and petition, with thanksgiving, present your requests to God. (Philippians 4:6)

Chapter Six

TELL IT TO YOUR CHILDREN, and let your children tell it to their children, and their children to the next generation. (Joel 1:3)

TELL IT TO YOUR CHILDREN, and let your children tell it to their children, and their children to the next generation. (Joel 1:3)

TELL IT TO YOUR CHILDREN, and let your children tell it to their children, and their children to the next generation. (Joel 1:3)

TELL IT TO YOUR CHILDREN, and let your children tell it to their children, and their children to the next generation. (Joel 1:3)

TELL IT TO YOUR CHILDREN, and let your children tell it to their children, and their children to the next generation. (Joel 1:3)

TRAIN A CHILD IN THE way he should go, and when he is old he will not turn from it. (Proverbs 22:6)

TRAIN A CHILD IN THE way he should go, and when he is old he will not turn from it. (Proverbs 22:6)

TRAIN A CHILD IN THE way he should go, and when he is old he will not turn from it. (Proverbs 22:6)

TRAIN A CHILD IN THE way he should go, and when he is old he will not turn from it. (Proverbs 22:6)

TRAIN A CHILD IN THE way he should go, and when he is old he will not turn from it. (Proverbs 22:6)

Chapter Seven

HE ANSWERED: "LOVE THE LORD your God with all your heart and with all your soul and with all your strength and with all your mind . . . " (Luke 10:27a)

HE ANSWERED: "LOVE THE LORD your God with all your heart and with all your soul and with all your strength and with all your mind . . . " (Luke 10:27a)

HE ANSWERED: "LOVE THE LORD your God with all your heart and with all your soul and with all your strength and with all your mind . . . " (Luke 10:27a)

HE ANSWERED: "LOVE THE LORD your God with all your heart and with all your soul and with all your strength and with all your mind . . . " (Luke 10:27a)

HE ANSWERED: "LOVE THE LORD your God with all your heart and with all your soul and with all your strength and with all your mind . . . " (Luke 10:27a)

DO NOT CONFORM ANY LONGER to the pattern of this world, but be transformed by the renewing of your mind . . . (Romans 12:2a)

DO NOT CONFORM ANY LONGER to the pattern of this world, but be transformed by the renewing of your mind . . . (Romans 12:2a)

DO NOT CONFORM ANY LONGER to the pattern of this world, but be transformed by the renewing of your mind . . . (Romans 12:2a)

DO NOT CONFORM ANY LONGER to the pattern of this world, but be transformed by the renewing of your mind . . . (Romans 12:2a)

DO NOT CONFORM ANY LONGER to the pattern of this world, but be transformed by the renewing of your mind . . . (Romans 12:2a)

Chapter Eight

BUT GOD DEMONSTRATES HIS OWN love for us in this: While we were still sinners, Christ died for us. (Romans 5:8)

BUT GOD DEMONSTRATES HIS OWN love for us in this: While we were still sinners, Christ died for us. (Romans 5:8)

BUT GOD DEMONSTRATES HIS OWN love for us in this: While we were still sinners, Christ died for us. (Romans 5:8)

BUT GOD DEMONSTRATES HIS OWN love for us in this: While we were still sinners, Christ died for us. (Romans 5:8)

BUT GOD DEMONSTRATES HIS OWN love for us in this: While we were still sinners, Christ died for us. (Romans 5:8)

THEREFORE, I URGE YOU, BROTHERS, in view of God's mercy, to offer your bodies as living sacrifices, holy and pleasing to God – this is your spiritual act of worship. (Romans 12:1)

THEREFORE, I URGE YOU, BROTHERS, in view of God's mercy, to offer your bodies as living sacrifices, holy and pleasing to God – this is your spiritual act of worship. (Romans 12:1)

THEREFORE, I URGE YOU, BROTHERS, in view of God's mercy, to offer your bodies as living sacrifices, holy and pleasing to God – this is your spiritual act of worship. (Romans 12:1)

THEREFORE, I URGE YOU, BROTHERS, in view of God's mercy, to offer your bodies as living sacrifices, holy and pleasing to God – this is your spiritual act of worship. (Romans 12:1)

THEREFORE, I URGE YOU, BROTHERS, in view of God's mercy, to offer your bodies as living sacrifices, holy and pleasing to God – this is your spiritual act of worship. (Romans 12:1)

Continuing Your Journey

Recommended Reading

WE HOPE YOU'VE THOROUGHLY ENJOYED the *Declutter Now! Study Guide* and pray you've made significant headway decluttering various areas of your life. As you continue on your journey, you may be inclined to tap into resources that further develop the doors opened and progress made through this study. There are more resources available than room to list them, but we'll offer some of our favorites to get you going. If you dig up any of your own, please do your due diligence to make sure the source is credible. We don't necessarily subscribe to, nor endorse, all the information presented in every book listed here. It's impossible to agree with everyone all the time—heck, we don't even expect you to agree with us all the time either! We do, however, believe the following provides legitimate self-help material from trustworthy experts.

TOTAL HOME MAKEOVER: A 20-DAY PLAN TO RENEW YOUR SPACE AND SPIRIT by Renee Metzler, Ambassador International, 2012. "*Total Home Makeover* is a complete home management course. During your journey, get yourself, your family, and your home all paddling in the same direction, toward order."

SETTING HEALTHY BOUNDARIES SERIES by Allison Bottke, Harvest House Publishing. There are (5) different *Setting Boundaries* books which include 'With Difficult People', 'With Food', 'for Women', 'With your Aging Parents' and 'With Your Adult Children'. Ms. Bottke offers help and healing through her six steps to SANITY. Check out her website at http://www.settingboundariesbooks.com.

BOUNDARIES: WHEN TO SAY YES, WHEN TO SAY NO, TO TAKE CONTROL OF YOUR LIFe by Henry Cloud and John Townsend, Zondervan, 1992. "Often, Christians focus so much on being loving and unselfish that they forget their own limits and limitations. When confronted with their lack of boundaries, they ask: Can I set limits and still be a loving person? What are legitimate boundaries? What if someone is upset or hurt by my boundaries? How do I answer someone who wants my time, love, energy, or money? Aren't boundaries selfish? Why do I feel guilty or afraid when I consider setting boundaries? Dr. Henry Cloud and Dr. John Townsend offer biblically-based answers to these and other tough questions, showing us how to set healthy boundaries with our parents, spouses, children, friends, co-workers, and even ourselves."

THE TOTAL MONEY MAKEOVER: A PROVEN PLAN FOR FINANCIAL FITNESS by Dave Ramsey, 3rd Edition, Thomas Nelson, 2009. "Ramsey debunks the many myths of money (exposing the dangers of cash advance, rent-to-own, debt consolidation) and attacks the illusions and downright deceptions of the American dream, which encourages nothing but over-spending and massive amounts of debt. 'Don't even consider keeping up with the Joneses,' Ramsey declares in his typically candid style. 'They're broke!' *The Total Money Makeover* isn't theory. It works every single time. It works because it is simple. It works because it gets to the heart of the money problems: you."

MORE MONEY IN TOUGH TIMES: DISCOVER THE $10,000 YOU NEVER KNEW YOU HAD by Tom L. Schneider and Lindy Schneider, Peaks Publishing, 2013. "In these tough economic times, everyone is look-ing for ways to help make ends meet. The authors, America's Money Archaeologists, show you over 100 ways to 'find' money you never knew you had. By making simple changes to how you spend your money, you can save thousands of dollars a year and still live well. Wise spending doesn't have to be painful."

QUITTER: CLOSING THE GAP BETWEEN YOUR DAY JOB & YOUR DREAM JOB by Jon Acuff, Lampo Press, 2011. "All too often, we hear that dream-ing big means you quit your day job, sell everything you own, and move to Guam. But what if there were a different way? What if you could blow up your dream without blowing up your life? What if you could go for broke without going broke? What if you could start today? What if you already have everything you need to begin? From figuring out what your dream is to quitting in a way that exponentially increases your chance of success, *Quitter* is full of inspiring stories and actionable advice. This book is based on 12 years of cubicle living and Jon Acuff's true story of cultivating a dream job that changed his life and the world in the process."

CHOOSE MORE, LOSE MORE FOR LIFE by Chris Powell, Hyperion, 2013. "At the center of Chris Powell's *Choose More, Lose More for Life* is Chris's carb-cycling plan, which kicks your metabolism into full gear by alternating between low- and high-carb days. Never carb-cycled before? No problem. Powell provides all the information you need to get started and see immediate results. Been carb-cycling but need to shake things up? This book provides four different cycles—Easy, Classic, Turbo, and Fit—to help you find a plan that fits you. Chris also understands that weight loss plateaus when we get bored. So in this book, he focuses on choices—including more than twenty new workouts called Nine-Minute Missions—that pack maximum results into minimal time. He also offers more delicious and easy recipes to keep you eating well, more tracking logs to keep you motivated, and more success stories to inspire you as you write your own—one that lasts for the rest of your life."

POSITIVE PARENTING WITH A PLAN (GRADES K-12): F.A.M.I.L.Y. RULES by Matthew A. Johnson, Publication Consultants, 2002. "There is no other parenting program out there like this one. If you want things to actually change in your home with a spelled out game plan for implementing the program from A-Z, then you've finally found it. If you correctly and consistently implement this program in your home, then expect things to get a whole lot better."

MAKING CHILDREN MIND WITHOUT LOSING YOURS by Kevin Leman, 2nd edition, Revell 2005. "Raising children these days can be daunting. But if anyone understands why children behave the way they do, it's Dr. Kevin Leman. He equips parents with seven principles of Reality Discipline, a loving no-nonsense parenting approach that really works."

BATTLEFIELD OF THE MIND: WINNING THE BATTLE IN YOUR MIND by Joyce Meyer, FaithWords, 2011. "Worry, doubt, confusion, depression, anger, and feelings of condemnation: all these are attacks on the mind. If readers suffer from negative thoughts, they can take heart! Joyce Meyer shows readers how to change their lives by changing their minds. She teaches how to deal with thousands of thoughts that people think every day and how to focus the mind the way God thinks. And she shares the trials, tragedies, and ultimate victories from her own marriage, family, and ministry that led her to wondrous, life-transforming truth—and reveals her thoughts and feelings every step of the way."

FEARLESS, Max Lucado, Thomas Nelson, 2012 reprint. "Imagine your life, wholly untouched by angst. What if faith, not fear, was your default reaction to threats? If you could hover a fear magnet over your heart and extract every last shaving of dread, insecurity, or doubt, what would remain? Envision a day, just one day, where you could trust more and fear less. Can you imagine your life without fear?"

FORGIVENESS IS NOT AN OPTION: A JOURNEY TO FREEDOM AND HEALING by Anna McCarthy, Ambassador International, 2012. "How do you forgive the unforgiveable? Is it possible to truly be free from what others have done to you? Each of us has a story and has experienced hurt in some area of our lives. Whether in childhood, adolescence, or adulthood, we all have experienced pain and disappointment. If not dealt with, these wounds begin to impact our everyday life at a crippling rate. Addressing a broad spectrum of issues from common offenses to abuse and betrayal, the author leaves no question as to God's opinion of mistreatment, and how we can heal and live a life of freedom from our past and present hurts."

SOUL DETOX: CLEAN LIVING IN A CONTAMINATED WORLD by Craig Groeschel, Zondervan, 2012. "Soul Detox examines the toxins that assault us daily, including toxic influences, toxic emotions, and toxic behaviors. By examining the toxins that assault us daily, this book offers the ultimate spiritual intervention with ways to remain clean, pure, and focused on the standard of God's holiness."

PRAYER: DOES IT MAKE ANY DIFFERENCE? by Philip Yancey, Zondervan, 2010. "Philip Yancey explores the intimate place where God and humans meet in prayer. Polls reveal that 90 percent of people pray. Yet prayer, which should be the most nourishing and uplifting time of the believer's day, can also be frustrating, confusing, and fraught with mystery. Writing as a fellow pilgrim, Yancey probes such questions as: ★Is God listening? ★Why should God care about me? ★If God knows everything, what's the point of prayer? ★Why do answers to prayer seem so inconsistent? ★Why does God sometimes seem close and sometimes seem far away? ★How can I make prayer more satisfying? Yancey tackles the tough questions and in the process comes up with a fresh new approach to this timeless topic. 'I have learned to pray as a privilege, not a duty,' he says, and he invites you to join him on this all-important journey."

And last but not least . . .

THERE ARE A ZILLION HOW-TO books on decluttering physical space, home organization, and innovative storage solutions. A simple Amazon search with any variety of key words will bring up more choices than you can imagine. There are books on organizing specific areas such as your kitchen or garage, creative solutions for small spaces, and practical ideas for storage. Whatever challenge you are faced with, help is out there!

MANY, MANY BLESSINGS ON YOUR CONTINUED DECLUTTERING JOURNEY!

For more information about
Lindon & Sherry Gareis
&
Declutter Now!

please visit:

www.actionplanministries.com
declutternow@actionplanministries.com
@actionplanmin
facebook.com/declutternow
youtube.com/actionplanmin
linkedin.com/in/actionplanministries
google.com/+actionplanministries
pinterest.com/actionplanmin

For more information about
AMBASSADOR INTERNATIONAL
please visit:

www.ambassador-international.com
@AmbassadorIntl
www.facebook.com/AmbassadorIntl